LETTERS FROM THE EARTH

is

unexpected treasure—
a vintage harvest of heretofore
unpublishable Twain from the
papers of America's greatest humorist

"Twain in the raw,
   jeering, brilliant, pulverizing."

— PAUL CARROLL,
Chicago Daily News

". . . The attitude is that of Swift, the
intellectual contempt is that of Voltaire, and
the imagination is that of one of
the great masters of American writing."

— HOWARD MUMFORD JONES,
The New York Times

"There may be a shock in store for readers
   who know Mark Twain only through
   The Adventures of Tom Sawyer *or through*
   The Adventures of Huckleberry Finn . . .
   a tremendously important revelation of one of
   America's greatest writers . . . dynamite."

—*Kansas City Times*

MARK TWAIN

LETTERS
FROM THE EARTH

EDITED BY BERNARD DeVOTO

WITH A PREFACE BY HENRY NASH SMITH

PERENNIAL LIBRARY

HARPER & ROW, PUBLISHERS

NEW YORK, EVANSTON, SAN FRANCISCO, LONDON

Contents

Preface

In his will Mark Twain directed the Trustees of his Estate to confer with his daughter Clara and Albert B. Paine, his biographer, concerning the administration of his "literary productions." Paine served as literary executor from 1910, when Mark Twain died, until his own death in 1937. During this period he published his three-volume biography, two volumes of letters, and a half-dozen other books drawn from the Mark Twain Papers. Shortly after Paine's death Harper & Brothers recommended to the Trustees that the late Bernard DeVoto, author of *Mark Twain's America* (1932) and at that time editor of *The Saturday Review of Literature*, should be asked to take over the task of preparing for publication further material selected from the thousands of pages of unpublished writings by Mark Twain.

DeVoto recommended that three volumes should be brought out: (1) selections from the Autobiographical Dictation to supplement those edited by Paine; (2) a volume of letters; and (3) a collection of sketches and other short pieces. He began work at once on the third item, and in March, 1939, submitted to the Trustees the manuscript of *Letters from the Earth*, "ready for the printer." But when Clara Clemens read the manuscript she objected to the publication of certain parts of it on the ground that they presented a distorted view of her father's ideas and attitudes. The project was accordingly dropped, and the work has lain unpublished for more than twenty years in the successive depositories of the Mark Twain Papers, at Harvard, the Huntington Library, and the University of California, Berkeley.

During these two decades a long series of scholarly and critical studies—including DeVoto's own authoritative *Mark Twain at Work* (1942)—has demonstrated that the celebrated humorist was also a great artist. He now belongs beyond question among the major American writers. Since 1960, the fiftieth anniversary of Mark Twain's death, at least a dozen books about him have been published. In this abundance of knowledge and interpretation all his writings can be allowed to speak for themselves, and Clara Clemens has withdrawn her objections to the publication of *Letters from the Earth.* The book is now presented as DeVoto edited it in 1939, with only one or two minor changes in his editorial comments to take account of subsequent events.

The volume falls into two main parts: a first section, comprising "Letters from the Earth," "Papers of the Adam Family," and "Letter to the Earth," that exhibits the astonishingly inventive play of Mark Twain's imagination about Biblical themes, or lunges out in satire of the world he lived in; and a more miscellaneous second section, containing DeVoto's selections from the remaining unpublished manuscripts in the Mark Twain Papers. These shorter pieces were written at intervals during four decades of Mark Twain's career and range in mood from a whimsical tale about cats he improvised for his children to the nightmare sea voyage of "The Great Dark." Several of them have been published separately since 1939, as is indicated in the Bibliographical Note, but they are included here in order to preserve the integrity of DeVoto's editorial intention.

For some of the items in the collection DeVoto provided explanatory comments, which are printed in italics. He also wrote notes to be placed at the back of the book, mainly but not exclusively about problems of dating. His occasional footnotes are signed with his initials ("B. DV.") to distinguish them from Mark Twain's footnotes, which are labeled "M.T." It should be kept in mind that since Mark Twain did not prepare these manuscripts for the press, they contain minor errors and inconsistencies of form which DeVoto corrected in order to produce a readable text.

Mrs. Bernard DeVoto has kindly given her consent to the publication of what is in a double sense a posthumous work.

Berkeley
March, 1962

HENRY NASH SMITH
Literary Editor
of the Mark Twain Papers

LETTERS
FROM THE EARTH

Letters from the Earth

THE Creator sat upon the throne, thinking. Behind him stretched the illimitable continent of heaven, steeped in a glory of light and color; before him rose the black night of Space, like a wall. His mighty bulk towered rugged and mountain-like into the zenith, and His divine head blazed there like a distant sun. At His feet stood three colossal figures, diminished to extinction, almost, by contrast—archangels—their heads level with His ankle-bone.

When the Creator had finished thinking, He said, "I have thought. Behold!"

He lifted His hand, and from it burst a fountain-spray of fire, a million stupendous suns, which clove the blackness and soared, away and away and away, diminishing in magnitude and intensity as they pierced the far frontiers of Space, until at last they were but as diamond nailheads sparkling under the domed vast roof of the universe.

At the end of an hour the Grand Council was dismissed.

They left the Presence impressed and thoughtful, and retired to a private place, where they might talk with freedom. None of the three seemed to want to begin, though all wanted somebody to do it. Each was burning to discuss the great event, but would prefer not to commit himself till he should know how the others regarded it. So there was some aimless and halting conversation about matters of no consequence, and this dragged tediously along, arriving nowhere, until at last the archangel Satan gathered his courage together—of which he had a very good supply—and broke ground. He said: "We know what we are here to talk about, my lords, and we may as well put pretense aside, and begin. If this is the opinion of the Council—"

"It is, it is!" said Gabriel and Michael, gratefully interrupting.

"Very well, then, let us proceed. We have witnessed a wonderful thing; as to that, we are necessarily agreed. As to the value of it—if it has any—that is a matter which does not personally concern us. We can have as many opinions about it as we like, and that is our limit. We have no vote. I think Space was well enough, just as it was, and useful, too. Cold and dark—a restful place, now and then, after a season of the overdelicate climate and trying splendors of heaven. But these are details of no considerable moment; the new feature, the immense feature, is—what, gentlemen?"

"The invention and introduction of automatic, unsupervised, self-regulating *law* for the government of those myriads of whirling and racing suns and worlds!"

"That is it!" said Satan. "You perceive that it is a stupendous idea. Nothing approaching it has been evolved from the Master Intellect before. Law—*Automatic* Law—exact and unvarying Law—requiring no watching, no correcting, no readjusting while the eternities endure! He said those countless vast bodies would plunge through the wastes of Space ages and ages, at unimaginable speed, around stupendous orbits, yet never collide, and never lengthen nor shorten their orbital periods by so much as the hundredth part of a second in two thousand years! That is the new miracle, and the greatest of all—*Automatic Law!* And He gave it a name—the LAW OF NATURE—and said Natural Law is the LAW OF GOD—interchangeable names for one and the same thing."

"Yes," said Michael, "and He said He would establish Natural Law—the Law of God—throughout His dominions, and its authority should be supreme and inviolable."

"Also," said Gabriel, "He said He would by and by create animals, and place them, likewise, under the authority of that Law."

"Yes," said Satan, "I heard Him, but did not understand. What *is* animals, Gabriel?"

"Ah, how should I know? How should any of us know? It is a new word."

[*Interval of three centuries, celestial time—the equivalent of a hundred million years, earthly time. Enter a Messenger-Angel.*]

"My lords, He is making animals. Will it please you to come and see?"

They went, they saw, and were perplexed. Deeply perplexed —and the Creator noticed it, and said, "Ask. I will answer."

"Divine One," said Satan, making obeisance, "what are they for?"

"They are an experiment in Morals and Conduct. Observe them, and be instructed."

There were thousands of them. They were full of activities. Busy, all busy—mainly in persecuting each other. Satan remarked—after examining one of them through a powerful microscope: "This large beast is killing weaker animals, Divine One."

"The tiger—yes. The law of his nature is ferocity. The law of his nature is the Law of God. He cannot disobey it."

"Then in obeying it he commits no offense, Divine One?"

"No, he is blameless."

"This other creature, here, is timid, Divine One, and suffers death without resisting."

"The rabbit—yes. He is without courage. It is the law of his nature—the Law of God. He must obey it."

"Then he cannot honorably be required to go counter to his nature and resist, Divine One?"

"No. No creature can be honorably required to go counter to the law of his nature—the Law of God."

After a long time and many questions, Satan said, "The spider kills the fly, and eats it; the bird kills the spider and eats it; the wildcat kills the goose; the—well, they all kill each other. It is murder all along the line. Here are countless multitudes of creatures, and they all kill, kill, kill, they are all murderers. And they are not to blame, Divine One?"

"They are not to blame. It is the law of their nature. And always the law of nature is the Law of God. Now—observe—behold! A new creature—and the masterpiece—*Man!*"

Men, women, children, they came swarming in flocks, in droves, in millions.

"What shall you do with them, Divine One?"

"Put into each individual, in differing shades and degrees, all the various Moral Qualities, in mass, that have been distributed, a single distinguishing characteristic at a time, among the nonspeaking animal world—courage, cowardice, ferocity, gentleness, fairness, justice, cunning, treachery, magnanimity, cruelty, malice, malignity, lust, mercy, pity, purity, selfishness, sweetness, honor, love, hate, baseness, nobility, loyalty, falsity, veracity, untruthfulness—each human being shall have *all* of these in him, and they will constitute his nature. In some, there will be high and fine characteristics which will submerge the evil ones, and those will be called good men; in others the evil characteristics will have dominion, and those will be called bad men. Observe—behold—they vanish!"

"Whither are they gone, Divine One?"

"To the earth—they and all their fellow animals."

"What is the earth?"

"A small globe I made, a time, two times and a half ago. You saw it, but did not notice it in the explosion of worlds and suns that sprayed from my hand. Man is an experiment, the other animals are another experiment. Time will show whether they were worth the trouble. The exhibition is over; you may take your leave, my lords."

Several days passed by.

This stands for a long stretch of (our) time, since in heaven a day is as a thousand years.

Satan had been making admiring remarks about certain of the Creator's sparkling industries—remarks which, being read between the lines, were sarcasms. He had made them confidentially to his safe friends the other archangels, but they had been overheard by some ordinary angels and reported at Headquarters.

He was ordered into banishment for a day—the celestial day. It was a punishment he was used to, on account of his too flexible tongue. Formerly he had been deported into Space, there being nowhither else to send him, and had flapped tediously around there in the eternal night and the Arctic chill; but now it occurred to him to push on and hunt up the earth and see how the Human-Race experiment was coming along.

By and by he wrote home—very privately—to St. Michael and St. Gabriel about it.

SATAN'S LETTER

This is a strange place, an extraordinary place, and interesting. There is nothing resembling it at home. The people are all insane, the other animals are all insane, the earth is insane, Nature itself is insane. Man is a marvelous curiosity. When he is at his very very best he is a sort of low grade nickel-plated angel; at his worst he is unspeakable, unimaginable; and first and last and all the time he is a sarcasm. Yet he blandly and in all sincerity calls himself the "noblest work of God." This is the truth I am telling you. And this is not a new idea with him, he has talked it through all the ages, and believed it. Believed it, and found nobody among all his race to laugh at it.

Moreover—if I may put another strain upon you—he thinks he is the Creator's pet. He believes the Creator is proud of him; he even believes the Creator loves him; has a passion for him; sits up nights to admire him; yes, and watch over him and keep him out of trouble. He prays to Him, and thinks He listens. Isn't it a quaint idea? Fills his prayers with crude and bald and florid flatteries of Him, and thinks He sits and purrs over these extravagancies and enjoys them. He prays for help, and favor, and protection, every day; and does it with hopefulness and confidence, too, although no prayer of his has ever been answered. The daily affront, the daily defeat, do not discourage him, he goes on praying just the same. There is something almost fine about this perseverance. I must put one more strain upon you: he thinks he is going to heaven!

He has salaried teachers who tell him that. They also tell him there is a hell, of everlasting fire, and that he will go to it if he doesn't keep the Commandments. What are the Commandments? They are a curiosity. I will tell you about them by and by.

LETTER II

"I have told you nothing about man that is not true." You must pardon me if I repeat that remark now and then in these letters; I want you to take seriously the things I am telling you, and I feel that if I were in your place and you in mine, I should need that reminder from time to time, to keep my credulity from flagging.

For there is nothing about man that is not strange to an immortal. He looks at nothing as we look at it, his sense of proportion is quite different from ours, and his sense of values is so widely divergent from ours, that with all our large intellectual powers it is not likely that even the most gifted among us would ever be quite able to understand it.

For instance, take this sample: he has imagined a heaven, and has left entirely out of it the supremest of all his delights, the one ecstasy that stands first and foremost in the heart of every individual of his race—and of ours—sexual intercourse!

It is as if a lost and perishing person in a roasting desert should be told by a rescuer he might choose and have all longed-for things but one, and he should elect to leave out water!

His heaven is like himself: strange, interesting, astonishing, grotesque. I give you my word, it has not a single feature in it that he *actually values*. It consists—utterly and entirely—of diversions which he cares next to nothing about, here in the earth, yet is quite sure he will like in heaven. Isn't it curious? Isn't it interesting? You must not think I am exaggerating, for it is not so. I will give you details.

Most men do not sing, most men cannot sing, most men will not stay where others are singing if it be continued more than two hours. Note that.

Only about two men in a hundred can play upon a musical instrument, and not four in a hundred have any wish to learn how. Set that down.

Many men pray, not many of them like to do it. A few pray long, the others make a short cut.

More men go to church than want to.

To forty-nine men in fifty the Sabbath Day is a dreary, dreary bore.

Of all the men in a church on a Sunday, two-thirds are tired when the service is half over, and the rest before it is finished.

The gladdest moment for all of them is when the preacher uplifts his hands for the benediction. You can hear the soft rustle of relief that sweeps the house, and you recognize that it is eloquent with gratitude.

All nations look down upon all other nations.

All nations dislike all other nations.

All white nations despise all colored nations, of whatever hue, and oppress them when they can.

White men will not associate with "niggers," nor marry them.

They will not allow them in their schools and churches.

All the world hates the Jew, and will not endure him except when he is rich.

I ask you to note all those particulars.

Further. All sane people detest noise.

All people, sane or insane, like to have variety in their life. Monotony quickly wearies them.

Every man, according to the mental equipment that has fallen to his share, exercises his intellect constantly, ceaselessly, and this exercise makes up a vast and valued and essential part of his life. The lowest intellect, like the highest, possesses a skill of some kind and takes a keen pleasure in testing it, proving it, perfecting it. The urchin who is his comrade's superior in games is as diligent and as enthusiastic in his practice as are the sculptor, the painter, the pianist, the mathematician and the rest. Not one of them could be happy if his talent were put under an interdict.

Now then, you have the facts. You know what the human race enjoys, and what it doesn't enjoy. It has invented a heaven, out of its own head, all by itself: guess what it is like! In fifteen hundred eternities you couldn't do it. The ablest mind known to you or me in fifty million aeons couldn't do it. Very well, I will tell you about it.

1. First of all, I recall to your attention the extraordinary fact with which I began. To wit, that the human being, like the immortals, naturally places sexual intercourse far and away above all other joys—yet he has left it out of his heaven! The very thought of it excites him; opportunity sets him wild; in this state he will risk life, reputation, everything—even his queer heaven itself—to make good that opportunity and ride it to the overwhelming climax. From youth to middle age all men and all women prize copulation above all other pleasures combined, yet it is actually as I have said: it is not in their heaven; prayer takes its place.

They prize it thus highly; yet, like all their so-called "boons," it is a poor thing. At its very best and longest the act is brief beyond imagination—the imagination of an immortal, I mean. In the matter of repetition the man is limited—oh, quite beyond immortal conception. We who continue the act and its supremest ecstasies unbroken and without withdrawal for centuries, will never be able to understand or adequately pity the awful poverty of these people in that rich gift which, possessed as we possess it, makes all other possessions trivial and not worth the trouble of invoicing.

2. In man's heaven *everybody sings!* The man who did not sing on earth sings there; the man who could not sing on earth is able to do it there. This universal singing is not casual, not occasional, not relieved by intervals of quiet; it goes on, all day long, and every day, during a stretch of twelve hours. And *everybody stays;* whereas in the earth the place would be empty in two hours. The singing is of hymns alone. Nay, it is of *one* hymn alone. The words are always the same, in number they are only about a dozen, there is no rhyme, there is no poetry: "Hosannah, hosannah, hosannah, Lord God of Sabaoth, 'rah! 'rah! 'rah! siss!—boom! . . . a-a-ah!"

3. Meantime, every person is playing on a harp—those millions and millions!—whereas not more than twenty in the thousand of them could play an instrument in the earth, or ever wanted to.

Consider the deafening hurricane of sound—millions and millions of voices screaming at once and millions and millions of harps gritting their teeth at the same time! I ask you: is it hideous, is it odious, is it horrible?

Consider further: it is a praise service; a service of compliment, of flattery, of adulation! Do you ask who it is that is willing to endure this strange compliment, this insane compliment; and who not only endures it, but likes it, enjoys it, requires it, commands it? Hold your breath!

It is God! This race's God, I mean. He sits on his throne, attended by his four and twenty elders and some other dignitaries pertaining to his court, and looks out over his miles and miles of tempestuous worshipers, and smiles, and purrs, and nods his satisfaction northward, eastward, southward; as quaint and naïve a spectacle as has yet been imagined in this universe, I take it.

It is easy to see that the inventor of the heavens did not originate the idea, but copied it from the show-ceremonies of some sorry little sovereign State up in the back settlements of the Orient somewhere.

All sane white people hate noise; yet they have tranquilly accepted this kind of a heaven—without thinking, without reflection, without examination—and they actually want to go to it! Profoundly devout old gray-headed men put in a large part of their time dreaming of the happy day when they will lay down the cares of this life and enter into the joys of that place. Yet you can see how unreal it is to them, and how little it takes a grip upon them as being fact, for they make no practical preparation for the great change: you never see one of them with a harp, you never hear one of them sing.

As you have seen, that singular show is a service of praise: praise by hymn, praise by prostration. It takes the place of "church." Now then, in the earth these people cannot stand much church—an hour and a quarter is the limit, and they draw the line at once a week. That is to say, Sunday. One day in seven; and even then they do not look forward to it with longing. And so—consider what their heaven provides for them: "church" that lasts forever, and a Sabbath that has no end! They quickly weary of this brief hebdomadal Sabbath here, yet they long for that eternal one; they dream of it, they talk about it, they *think* they think they are going to enjoy it —with all their simple hearts they think they think they are going to be happy in it!

It is because they do not think at all; they only think they think. Whereas they can't think; not two human beings in ten thousand have anything to think with. And as to imagination —oh, well, look at their heaven! They accept it, they approve it, they admire it. That gives you their intellectual measure.

4. The inventor of their heaven empties into it all the nations of the earth, in one common jumble. All are on an equality absolute, no one of them ranking another; they have to be "brothers"; they have to mix together, pray together, harp together, hosannah together—whites, niggers, Jews, everybody— there's no distinction. Here in the earth all nations hate each other, and every one of them hates the Jew. Yet every pious person adores that heaven and wants to get into it. He really does. And when he is in a holy rapture he thinks he thinks that if he were only there he would take all the populace to his heart, and hug, and hug, and hug!

He is a marvel—man is! I would I knew who invented him.

5. Every man in the earth possesses some share of intellect, large or small; and be it large or be it small he takes a pride in it. Also his heart swells at mention of the names of the majestic intellectual chiefs of his race, and he loves the tale of their splendid achievements. For he is of their blood, and in honoring themselves they have honored him. Lo, what the mind of man can do! he cries; and calls the roll of the illustrious of all the ages; and points to the imperishable literatures they have given to the world, and the mechanical wonders they have invented, and the glories wherewith they have clothed science and the arts; and to them he uncovers, as to kings, and gives to them the profoundest homage, and the sincerest, his exultant heart can furnish—thus exalting intellect above all things else in his world, and enthroning it there under the arching skies in a supremacy unapproachable. And then he contrives a heaven that hasn't a rag of intellectuality in it anywhere!

Is it odd, is it curious, is it puzzling? It is exactly as I have said, incredible as it may sound. This sincere adorer of intellect and prodigal rewarder of its mighty services here in the earth has invented a religion and a heaven which pay no compliments to intellect, offer it no distinctions, fling to it no largess: in fact, never even mention it.

By this time you will have noticed that the human being's heaven has been thought out and constructed upon an absolutely definite plan; and that this plan is, that it shall contain, in labored detail, each and every imaginable thing that is repulsive to a man, and not a single thing he likes!

Very well, the further we proceed the more will this curious fact be apparent.

Make a note of it: in man's heaven there are no exercises for the intellect, nothing for it to live upon. It would rot there in a year—rot and stink. Rot and stink—and at that stage become holy. A blessed thing: for only the holy can stand the joys of that bedlam.

LETTER III

You have noticed that the human being is a curiosity. In times past he has had (and worn out and flung away) hundreds and hundreds of religions; today he has hundreds and hundreds of religions, and launches not fewer than three new ones every year. I could enlarge that number and still be within the facts.

One of his principal religions is called the Christian. A sketch of it will interest you. It is set forth in detail in a book containing two million words, called the Old and New Testaments. Also it has another name—The Word of God. For the Christian thinks every word of it was dictated by God—the one I have been speaking of.

It is full of interest. It has noble poetry in it; and some clever fables; and some blood-drenched history; and some good morals; and a wealth of obscenity; and upwards of a thousand lies.

This Bible is built mainly out of the fragments of older Bibles that had their day and crumbled to ruin. So it noticeably lacks in originality, necessarily. Its three or four most imposing and impressive events all happened in earlier Bibles; all its best precepts and rules of conduct came also from those Bibles; there are only two new things in it: hell, for one, and that singular heaven I have told you about.

What shall we do? If we believe, with these people, that their God invented these cruel things, we slander him; if we believe that these people invented them themselves, we slander them. It is an unpleasant dilemma in either case, for neither of these parties has done us any harm.

For the sake of tranquillity, let us take a side. Let us join forces with the people and put the whole ungracious burden upon *him*—heaven, hell, Bible and all. It does not seem right, it does not seem fair; and yet when you consider that heaven, and how crushingly charged it is with everything that is repulsive to a human being, how can we believe a human being invented it? And when I come to tell you about hell, the strain will be greater still, and you will be likely to say, No, a man would not provide that place, for either himself or anybody else; he simply couldn't.

That innocent Bible tells about the Creation. Of what—the universe? Yes, the universe. In six days!

God did it. He did not call it the universe—that name is modern. His whole attention was upon this world. He constructed it in five days—and then? It took him only one day to make twenty million suns and eighty million planets!

What were they for—according to his idea? To furnish light for this little toy-world. That was his whole purpose; he had no other. One of the twenty million suns (the smallest one) was to light it in the daytime, the rest were to help one of the universe's countless moons modify the darkness of its nights.

It is quite manifest that he believed his fresh-made skies were diamond-sown with those myriads of twinkling stars the moment his first-day's sun sank below the horizon; whereas, in fact, not a single star winked in that black vault until three years and a half after that memorable week's formidable industries had been completed.* Then one star appeared, all solitary and alone, and began to blink. Three years later another one appeared. The two blinked together for more than four years before a third joined them. At the end of the first hundred years there were not yet twenty-five stars twinkling in the wide wastes of those gloomy skies. At the end of a thousand years not enough stars were yet visible to make a show. At the end of a million years only half of the present array had sent their light over the telescopic frontiers, and it took another million for the rest to follow suit, as the vulgar phrase goes. There being at that time no telescope, their advent was not observed.

For three hundred years, now, the Christian astronomer has known that his Deity didn't make the stars in those tremen-

* It takes the light of the nearest star (61 Cygni) three and a half years to come to the earth, traveling at the rate of 186,000 miles per second. Arcturus had been shining 200 years before it was visible from the earth. Remoter stars gradually became visible after thousands and thousands of years.—THE EDITOR [M. T.]

dous six days; but the Christian astronomer does not enlarge upon that detail. Neither does the priest.

In his Book, God is eloquent in his praises of his mighty works, and calls them by the largest names he can find—thus indicating that he has a strong and just admiration of magnitudes; yet he made those millions of prodigious suns to light this wee little orb, instead of appointing this orb's little sun to dance attendance upon them. He mentions Arcturus in his Book—you remember Arcturus; we went there once. It is one of this earth's night lamps!—that giant globe which is fifty thousand times as large as this earth's sun, and compares with it as a melon compares with a cathedral.

However, the Sunday school still teaches the child that Arcturus was created to help light this earth, and the child grows up and continues to believe it long after he has found out that the probabilities are against its being so.

According to the Book and its servants the universe is only six thousand years old. It is only within the last hundred years that studious, inquiring minds have found out that it is nearer a hundred million.

During the Six Days, God created man and the other animals.

He made a man and a woman and placed them in a pleasant garden, along with the other creatures. They all lived together there in harmony and contentment and blooming youth for some time; then trouble came. God had warned the man and the woman that they must not eat of the fruit of a certain tree. And he added a most strange remark: he said that if they ate of it they should surely die. Strange, for the reason that inasmuch as they had never seen a sample of death they could not possibly know what he meant. Neither would he nor any other god have been able to make those ignorant children understand what was meant, without furnishing a sample. The mere word could have no meaning for them, any more than it would have for an infant of days.

Presently a serpent sought them out privately, and came to them walking upright, which was the way of serpents in those days. The serpent said the forbidden fruit would store their vacant minds with knowledge. So they ate it, which was quite natural, for man is so made that he eagerly wants to know; whereas the priest, like God, whose imitator and representative he is, has made it his business from the beginning to keep him from knowing any useful thing.

Adam and Eve ate the forbidden fruit, and at once a great light streamed into their dim heads. They had acquired knowledge. What knowledge—useful knowledge? No—merely knowledge that there was such a thing as good, and such a thing as evil, and how to do evil. They couldn't do it before. Therefore all their acts up to this time had been without stain, without blame, without offense.

But now they could do evil—and suffer for it; now they had acquired what the Church calls an invaluable possession, the Moral Sense; that sense which differentiates man from the beast and sets him above the beast. Instead of below the beast —where one would suppose his proper place would be, since he is always foul-minded and guilty and the beast always clean-minded and innocent. It is like valuing a watch that must go wrong, above a watch that can't.

The Church still prizes the Moral Sense as man's noblest asset today, although the Church knows God had a distinctly poor opinion of it and did what he could in his clumsy way to keep his happy Children of the Garden from acquiring it.

Very well, Adam and Eve now knew what evil was, and how to do it. They knew how to do various kinds of wrong things, and among them one principal one—the one God had his mind on principally. That one was the art and mystery of sexual intercourse. To them it was a magnificent discovery, and they stopped idling around and turned their entire attention to it, poor exultant young things!

In the midst of one of these celebrations they heard God walking among the bushes, which was an afternoon custom of his, and they were smitten with fright. Why? Because they were naked. They had not known it before. They had not minded it before; neither had God.

In that memorable moment immodesty was born; and some people have valued it ever since, though it would certainly puzzle them to explain why.

Adam and Eve entered the world naked and unashamed— naked and pure-minded; and no descendant of theirs has ever entered it otherwise. All have entered it naked, unashamed, and clean in mind. They have entered it modest. They had to acquire immodesty and the soiled mind; there was no other way to get it. A Christian mother's first duty is to soil her child's mind, and she does not neglect it. Her lad grows up to be a missionary, and goes to the innocent savage and to the civilized Japanese, and soils their minds. Whereupon they adopt immodesty, they conceal their bodies, they stop bathing naked together.

The convention miscalled modesty has no standard, and cannot have one, because it is opposed to nature and reason, and is therefore an artificiality and subject to anybody's whim, anybody's diseased caprice. And so, in India the refined lady covers her face and breasts and leaves her legs naked from the hips down, while the refined European lady covers her legs and exposes her face and her breasts. In lands inhabited by the innocent savage the refined European lady soon gets used to full-grown native stark-nakedness, and ceases to be offended by it. A highly cultivated French count and countess—unrelated to each other—who were marooned in their nightclothes, by shipwreck, upon an uninhabited island in the eighteenth century, were soon naked. Also ashamed—for a week. After that their nakedness did not trouble them, and they soon ceased to think about it.

You have never seen a person with clothes on. Oh, well, you haven't lost anything.

To proceed with the Biblical curiosities. Naturally you will think the threat to punish Adam and Eve for disobeying was of course not carried out, since they did not create themselves, nor their natures nor their impulses nor their weaknesses, and hence were not properly subject to anyone's commands, and not responsible to anybody for their acts. It will surprise you to know that the threat was carried out. Adam and Eve were punished, and that crime finds apologists unto this day. The sentence of death was executed.

As you perceive, the only person responsible for the couple's offense escaped; and not only escaped but became the executioner of the innocent.

In your country and mine we should have the privilege of making fun of this kind of morality, but it would be unkind to do it here. Many of these people have the reasoning faculty, but no one uses it in religious matters.

The best minds will tell you that when a man has begotten a child he is morally bound to tenderly care for it, protect it from hurt, shield it from disease, clothe it, feed it, bear with its waywardness, lay no hand upon it save in kindness and for its own good, and never in any case inflict upon it a wanton cruelty. God's treatment of his earthly children, every day and every night, is the exact opposite of all that, yet those best minds warmly justify these crimes, condone them, excuse

them, and indignantly refuse to regard them as crimes at all,
when he commits them. Your country and mine is an interesting one, but there is nothing there that is half so interesting
as the human mind.

Very well, God banished Adam and Eve from the Garden,
and eventually assassinated them. All for disobeying a command which he had no right to utter. But he did not stop
there, as you will see. He has one code of morals for himself,
and quite another for his children. He requires his children to
deal justly—and gently—with offenders, and forgive them
seventy-and-seven times; whereas he deals neither justly nor
gently with anyone, and he did not forgive the ignorant and
thoughtless first pair of juveniles even their first small offense
and say, "You may go free this time, I will give you another
chance."

On the contrary! He elected to punish their children, all
through the ages to the end of time, for a trifling offense
committed by others before they were born. He is punishing
them yet. In mild ways? No, in atrocious ones.

You would not suppose that this kind of a Being gets many
compliments. Undeceive yourself: the world calls him the
All-Just, the All-Righteous, the All-Good, the All-Merciful,
the All-Forgiving, the All-Truthful, the All-Loving, the Source
of All Morality. These sarcasms are uttered daily, all over the
world. But not as conscious sarcasms. No, they are meant
seriously: they are uttered without a smile.

LETTER IV

So the First Pair went forth from the Garden under a curse
—a permanent one. They had lost every pleasure they had
possessed before "The Fall"; and yet they were rich, for they
had gained one worth all the rest: they knew the Supreme
Art.

They practiced it diligently and were filled with contentment. The Deity ordered them to practice it. They obeyed,
this time. But it was just as well it was not forbidden, for they
would have practiced it anyhow, if a thousand Deities had
forbidden it.

Results followed. By the name of Cain and Abel. And these
had some sisters; and knew what to do with them. And so
there were some more results: Cain and Abel begot some

nephews and nieces. These, in their turn, begot some second cousins. At this point classification of relationships began to get difficult, and the attempt to keep it up was abandoned.

The pleasant labor of populating the world went on from age to age, and with prime efficiency; for in those happy days the sexes were still competent for the Supreme Art when by rights they ought to have been dead eight hundred years. The sweeter sex, the dearer sex, the lovelier sex was manifestly at its very best, then, for it was even able to attract gods. Real gods. They came down out of heaven and had wonderful times with those hot young blossoms. The Bible tells about it.

By help of those visiting foreigners the population grew and grew until it numbered several millions. But it was a disappointment to the Deity. He was dissatisfied with its morals; which in some respects were not any better than his own. Indeed they were an unflatteringly close imitation of his own. They were a very bad people, and as he knew of no way to reform them, he wisely concluded to abolish them. This is the only really enlightened and superior idea his Bible has credited him with, and it would have made his reputation for all time if he could only have kept to it and carried it out. But he was always unstable—except in his advertisements—and his good resolution broke down. He took a pride in man; man was his finest invention; man was his pet, after the housefly, and he could not bear to lose him wholly; so he finally decided to save a sample of him and drown the rest.

Nothing could be more characteristic of him. He created all those infamous people, and he alone was responsible for their conduct. Not one of them deserved death, yet it was certainly good policy to extinguish them; especially since in creating them the master crime had already been committed, and to allow them to go on procreating would be a distinct addition to the crime. But at the same time there could be no justice, no fairness, in any favoritism—all should be drowned or none.

No, he would not have it so; he would save half a dozen and try the race over again. He was not able to foresee that it would go rotten again, for he is only the Far-Sighted One in his advertisements.

He saved out Noah and his family, and arranged to exterminate the rest. He planned an Ark, and Noah built it. Neither of them had ever built an Ark before, nor knew anything about Arks; and so something out of the common was to be expected.

It happened. Noah was a farmer, and although he knew what was required of the Ark he was quite incompetent to say whether this one would be large enough to meet the requirements or not (which it wasn't), so he ventured no advice. The Deity did not know it wasn't large enough, but took the chances and made no adequate measurements. In the end the ship fell far short of the necessities, and to this day the world still suffers for it.

Noah built the Ark. He built it the best he could, but left out most of the essentials. It had no rudder, it had no sails, it had no compass, it had no pumps, it had no charts, no leadlines, no anchors, no log, no light, no ventilation, and as for cargo room—which was the main thing—the less said about that the better. It was to be at sea eleven months, and would need fresh water enough to fill two Arks of its size—yet the additional Ark was not provided. Water from outside could not be utilized: half of it would be salt water, and men and land animals could not drink it.

For not only was a sample of man to be saved, but business samples of the other animals, too. You must understand that when Adam ate the apple in the Garden and learned how to multiply and replenish, the other animals learned the Art, too, by watching Adam. It was cunning of them, it was neat; for they got all that was worth having out of the apple without tasting it and afflicting themselves with the disastrous Moral Sense, the parent of all the immoralities.

LETTER V

Noah began to collect animals. There was to be one couple of each and every sort of creature that walked or crawled, or swam or flew, in the world of animated nature. We have to guess at how long it took to collect the creatures and how much it cost, for there is no record of these details. When Symmachus made preparation to introduce his young son to grown-up life in imperial Rome, he sent men to Asia, Africa and everywhere to collect wild animals for the arena-fights. It took the men three years to accumulate the animals and fetch them to Rome. Merely quadrupeds and alligators, you understand—no birds, no snakes, no frogs, no worms, no lice, no rats, no fleas, no ticks, no caterpillars, no spiders, no houseflies, no mosquitoes—nothing but just plain simple quadrupeds and alligators: and no quadrupeds except fighting ones. Yet it was as I have said: it took three years to collect them, and the cost of animals and transportation and the men's wages footed up $4,500,000.

How many animals? We do not know. But it was under five thousand, for that was the largest number ever gathered for those Roman shows, and it was Titus, not Symmachus, who made that collection. Those were mere baby museums, compared to Noah's contract. Of birds and beasts and fresh-water creatures he had to collect 146,000 kinds; and of insects upwards of two million species.

Thousands and thousands of those things are very difficult to catch, and if Noah had not given up and resigned, he would be on the job yet, as Leviticus used to say. However, I do not mean that he withdrew. No, he did not do that. He gathered as many creatures as he had room for, and then stopped.

If he had known all the requirements in the beginning, he would have been aware that what was needed was a fleet of Arks. But he did not know how many kinds of creatures there were, neither did his Chief. So he had no kangaroo, and no 'possum, and no Gila monster, and no ornithorhynchus, and lacked a multitude of other indispensable blessings which a loving Creator had provided for man and forgotten about, they having long ago wandered to a side of this world which he had never seen and with whose affairs he was not acquainted. And so everyone of them came within a hair of getting drowned.

They only escaped by an accident. There was not water enough to go around. Only enough was provided to flood one small corner of the globe—the rest of the globe was not then known, and was supposed to be nonexistent.

However, the thing that really and finally and definitely determined Noah to stop with enough species for purely business purposes and let the rest become extinct, was an incident of the last days: an excited stranger arrived with some most alarming news. He said he had been camping among some mountains and valleys about six hundred miles away, and he had seen a wonderful thing there: he stood upon a precipice overlooking a wide valley, and up the valley he saw a billowy black sea of strange animal life coming. Presently the creatures passed by, struggling, fighting, scrambling, screeching, snorting —horrible vast masses of tumultuous flesh! Sloths as big as an elephant; frogs as big as a cow; a megatherium and his harem huge beyond belief; saurians and saurians and saurians, group after group, family after family, species after species—a hundred feet long, thirty feet high, and twice as quarrelsome; one of them hit a perfectly blameless Durham bull a thump with its tail and sent it whizzing three hundred feet into the air and it fell at the man's feet with a sigh and was no more. The man said that these prodigious animals had heard about the Ark and were coming. Coming to get saved from the flood. And not coming in pairs, they were all coming: they did not know the passengers were restricted to pairs, the man said, and wouldn't care a rap for the regulations, anyway—they would sail in that Ark or know the reason why. The man said the Ark would not hold the half of them; and moreover they were coming hungry, and would eat up everything there was, including the menagerie and the family.

All these facts were suppressed, in the Biblical account. You find not a hint of them there. The whole thing is hushed up. Not even the names of those vast creatures are mentioned. It shows you that when people have left a reproachful vacancy in a contract they can be as shady about it in Bibles as elsewhere. Those powerful animals would be of inestimable value to man now, when transportation is so hard pressed and expensive, but they are all lost to him. All lost, and by Noah's fault. They all got drowned. Some of them as much as eight million years ago.

Very well, the stranger told his tale, and Noah saw that he must get away before the monsters arrived. He would have sailed at once, but the upholsterers and decorators of the housefly's drawing room still had some finishing touches to put on, and that lost him a day. Another day was lost in getting the flies aboard, there being sixty-eight billions of them and the Deity still afraid there might not be enough. Another day was lost in stowing forty tons of selected filth for the flies' sustenance.

Then at last, Noah sailed; and none too soon, for the Ark was only just sinking out of sight on the horizon when the monsters arrived, and added their lamentations to those of the multitude of weeping fathers and mothers and frightened little children who were clinging to the wave-washed rocks in the pouring rain and lifting imploring prayers to an All-Just and All-Forgiving and All-Pitying Being who had never answered a prayer since those crags were builded, grain by grain out of the sands, and would still not have answered one when the ages should have crumbled them to sand again.

LETTER VI

On the third day, about noon, it was found that a fly had been left behind. The return voyage turned out to be long and difficult, on account of the lack of chart and compass, and because of the changed aspects of all coasts, the steadily rising water having submerged some of the lower landmarks and given to higher ones an unfamiliar look; but after sixteen days of earnest and faithful seeking, the fly was found at last, and received on board with hymns of praise and gratitude, the Family standing meanwhile uncovered, out of reverence for its divine origin. It was weary and worn, and had suffered somewhat from the weather, but was otherwise in good estate. Men and their families had died of hunger on barren mountain tops, but it had not lacked for food, the multitudinous corpses furnishing it in rank and rotten richness. Thus was the sacred bird providentially preserved.

Providentially. That is the word. For the fly had not been left behind by accident. No, the hand of Providence was in it. There are no accidents. All things that happen, happen for a purpose. They are foreseen from the beginning of time, they are ordained from the beginning of time. From the dawn of Creation the Lord had foreseen that Noah, being alarmed and confused by the invasion of the prodigious brevet fossils, would prematurely fly to sea unprovided with a certain invaluable disease. He would have all the other diseases, and could distribute them among the new races of men as they appeared in the world, but he would lack one of the very best—typhoid fever; a malady which, when the circumstances are especially favorable, is able to utterly wreck a patient without killing him; for it can restore him to his feet with a long life in him, and yet deaf, dumb, blind, crippled, and idiotic. The housefly is its main disseminator, and is more competent and more calamitously effective than all the other distributors of the dreaded scourge put together. And so, by foreordination from the beginning of time, this fly was left behind to seek out a typhoid corpse and feed upon its corruptions and gaum its legs with the germs and transmit them to the re-peopled world for permanent business. From that one housefly, in the ages that have since elapsed, billions of sickbeds have been stocked, billions of wrecked bodies sent tottering about the earth, and billions of cemeteries recruited with the dead.

It is most difficult to understand the disposition of the Bible God, it is such a confusion of contradictions; of watery instabilities and iron firmnesses; of goody-goody abstract morals made out of words, and concreted hell-born ones made out of acts; of fleeting kindnesses repented of in permanent malignities.

However, when after much puzzling you get at the key to his disposition, you do at last arrive at a sort of understanding of it. With a most quaint and juvenile and astonishing frankness he has furnished that key himself. It is jealousy!

I expect that to take your breath away. You are aware—for I have already told you in an earlier letter—that among human beings jealousy ranks distinctly as a weakness; a trade-mark of small minds; a property of *all* small minds, yet a property which even the smallest is ashamed of; and when accused of its possession will lyingly deny it and resent the accusation as an insult.

Jealousy. Do not forget it, keep it in mind. It is the key. With it you will come to partly understand God as we go along; without it nobody can understand him. As I have said, he has openly held up this treasonous key himself, for all to see. He says, naïvely, outspokenly, and without suggestion of embarrassment: "I the Lord thy God am a jealous God."

You see, it is only another way of saying, "I the Lord thy God am a small God; a small God, and fretful about small things."

He was giving a warning: he could not bear the thought of any other God getting some of the Sunday compliments of this comical little human race—he wanted all of them for himself. He valued them. To him they were riches; just as tin money is to a Zulu.

But wait—I am not fair; I am misrepresenting him; prejudice is beguiling me into saying what is not true. He did not say he wanted all of the adulations; he said nothing about not being willing to share them with his fellow gods; what he said was, "Thou shalt have no other gods before me."

It is a quite different thing, and puts him in a much better light—I confess it. There was an abundance of gods, the woods were full of them, as the saying is, and all he demanded was that he should be ranked as high as the others—not above any of them, but not below any of them. He was willing that they should fertilize earthly virgins, but not on any better terms than he could have for himself in his turn. He wanted to be held their equal. This he insisted upon, in the clearest language: he would have no other gods before him. They could march abreast with him, but none of them could head the procession, and he did not claim the right to head it himself.

Do you think he was able to stick to that upright and creditable position? No. He could keep to a bad resolution forever, but he couldn't keep to a good one a month. By and by he threw this one aside and calmly claimed to be the only God in the entire universe.

As I was saying, jealousy is the key; all through his history it is present and prominent. It is the blood and bone of his disposition, it is the basis of his character. How small a thing can wreck his composure and disorder his judgment if it touches the raw of his jealousy! And nothing warms up this trait so quickly and so surely and so exaggeratedly as a suspicion that some competition with the god-Trust is impending. The fear that if Adam and Eve ate of the fruit of the Tree of Knowledge they would "be as gods" so fired his jealousy that his reason was affected, and he could not treat those poor creatures either fairly or charitably, or even refrain from dealing cruelly and criminally with their blameless posterity.

To this day his reason has never recovered from that shock; a wild nightmare of vengefulness has possessed him ever since, and he has almost bankrupted his native ingenuities in inventing pains and miseries and humiliations and heartbreaks wherewith to embitter the brief lives of Adam's descendants. Think of the diseases he has contrived for them! They are multitudinous; no book can name them all. And each one is a trap, set for an innocent victim.

The human being is a machine. An automatic machine. It is composed of thousands of complex and delicate mechanisms, which perform their functions harmoniously and perfectly, in accordance with laws devised for their governance, and over which the man himself has no authority, no mastership, no control. For each one of these thousands of mechanisms the Creator has planned an enemy, whose office is to harass it, pester it, persecute it, damage it, afflict it with pains, and miseries, and ultimate destruction. Not one has been overlooked.

From cradle to grave these enemies are always at work; they

know no rest, night or day. They are an army: an organized army; a besieging army; an assaulting army; an army that is alert, watchful, eager, merciless; an army that never relents, never grants a truce.

It moves by squad, by company, by battalion, by regiment, by brigade, by division, by army corps; upon occasion it masses its parts and moves upon mankind with its whole strength. It is the Creator's Grand Army, and he is the Commander-in-Chief. Along its battlefront its grisly banners wave their legends in the face of the sun: Disaster, Disease, and the rest.

Disease! That is the main force, the diligent force, the devastating force! It attacks the infant the moment it is born; it furnishes it one malady after another: croup, measles, mumps, bowel troubles, teething pains, scarlet fever, and other childhood specialties. It chases the child into youth and furnishes it some specialties for that time of life. It chases the youth into maturity, maturity into age, and age into the grave.

With these facts before you will you now try to guess man's chiefest pet name for this ferocious Commander-in-Chief? I will save you the trouble—but you must not laugh. It is Our Father in Heaven!

It is curious—the way the human mind works. The Christian begins with this straight proposition, this definite proposition, this inflexible and uncompromising proposition: God *is all-knowing, and all-powerful.*

This being the case, nothing can happen without his knowing beforehand that it is going to happen; nothing happens without his permission; nothing can happen that he chooses to prevent.

That is definite enough, isn't it? It makes the Creator distinctly responsible for everything that happens, doesn't it?

The Christian concedes it in that italicized sentence. Concedes it with feeling, with enthusiasm.

Then, having thus made the Creator responsible for all those pains and diseases and miseries above enumerated, and which he could have prevented, the gifted Christian blandly calls him Our Father!

It is as I tell you. He equips the Creator with every trait that goes to the making of a fiend, and then arrives at the conclusion that a fiend and a father are the same thing! Yet he would deny that a malevolent lunatic and a Sunday school superintendent are essentially the same. What do you think of the human mind? I mean, in case you think there is a human mind.

LETTER VII

Noah and his family were saved—if that could be called an advantage. I throw in the *if* for the reason that there has never been an intelligent person of the age of sixty who would consent to live his life over again. His or anyone else's. The Family were saved, yes, but they were not comfortable, for they were full of microbes. Full to the eyebrows; fat with them, obese with them; distended like balloons. It was a disagreeable condition, but it could not be helped, because enough microbes had to be saved to supply the future races of men with desolating diseases, and there were but eight persons on board to serve as hotels for them. The microbes were by far the most important part of the Ark's cargo, and the part the Creator was most anxious about and most infatuated with. They had to have good nourishment and pleasant accommodations. There were typhoid germs, and cholera germs, and hydrophobia germs, and lockjaw germs, and consumption germs, and black-plague germs, and some hundreds of other aristocrats, specially precious creations, golden bearers of God's love to man, blessed gifts of the infatuated Father to his children—all of which had to be sumptuously housed and richly entertained; these were located in the choicest places the interiors of the Family could furnish: in the lungs, in the heart, in the brain, in the kidneys, in the blood, in the guts. In the guts particularly. The great intestine was the favorite resort. There they gathered, by countless billions, and worked, and fed, and squirmed, and sang hymns of praise and thanksgiving; and at night when it was quiet you could hear the soft murmur of it. The large intestine was in effect their heaven. They stuffed it solid; they made it as rigid as a coil of gaspipe. They took pride in this. Their principal hymn made gratified reference to it:

> Constipation, O constipation,
> The joyful sound proclaim
> Till man's remotest entrail
> Shall praise its Maker's name.

The discomforts furnished by the Ark were many and various. The family had to live right in the presence of the multitudinous animals, and breathe the distressing stench they made and be deafened day and night with the thunder-crash of noise their roarings and screechings produced; and in addition to these intolerable discomforts it was a peculiarly trying place for the ladies, for they could look in no direction without seeing some thousands of the creatures engaged in multiplying and replenishing. And then, there were the flies. They swarmed everywhere, and persecuted the Family all day long. They were the first animals up, in the morning, and the last ones down, at night. But they must not be killed, they must not be injured, they were sacred, their origin was divine, they were the special pets of the Creator, his darlings.

By and by the other creatures would be distributed here and there about the earth—scattered: the tigers to India, the lions and the elephants to the vacant desert and the secret places of the jungle, the birds to the boundless regions of empty space, the insects to one or another climate, according to nature and requirement; but the fly? He is of no nationality; all the climates are his home, all the globe is his province, all creatures that breathe are his prey, and unto them all he is a scourge and a hell.

To man he is a divine ambassador, a minister plenipotentiary, the Creator's special representative. He infests him in his cradle; clings in bunches to his gummy eyelids; buzzes and bites and harries him, robbing him of his sleep and his weary mother of her strength in those long vigils which she devotes to protecting her child from this pest's persecutions. The fly harries the sick man in his home, in the hospital, even on his deathbed at his last gasp. Pesters him at his meals; previously hunts up patients suffering from loathsome and deadly diseases; wades in their sores, gaums its legs with a million death-dealing germs; then comes to that healthy man's table and wipes these things off on the butter and discharges a bowel-load of typhoid germs and excrement on his batter-cakes. The housefly wrecks more human constitutions and destroys more human lives than all God's multitude of misery-messengers and death-agents put together.

Shem was full of hookworms. It is wonderful, the thorough and comprehensive study which the Creator devoted to the great work of making man miserable. I have said he devised a special affliction-agent for each and every detail of man's structure, overlooking not a single one, and I said the truth. Many poor people have to go barefoot, because they cannot afford shoes. The Creator saw his opportunity. I will remark, in pas-

sing, that he always has his eye on the poor. Nine-tenths of his
disease-inventions were intended for the poor, and they get
them. The well-to-do get only what is left over. Do not suspect
me of speaking unheedfully, for it is not so: the vast bulk of the
Creator's affliction-inventions are specially designed for the persecution of the poor. You could guess this by the fact that one
of the pulpit's finest and commonest names for the Creator is
"The Friend of the Poor." Under no circumstances does the
pulpit ever pay the Creator a compliment that has a vestige of
truth in it. The poor's most implacable and unwearying enemy
is their Father in Heaven. The poor's only real friend is their
fellow man. He is sorry for them, he pities them, and he shows
it by his deeds. He does much to relieve their distresses; and
in every case their Father in Heaven gets the credit of it.

Just so with diseases. If science exterminates a disease which
has been working for God, it is God that gets the credit, and all
the pulpits break into grateful advertising-raptures and call attention to how good he is! Yes, he has done it. Perhaps he has
waited a thousand years before doing it. That is nothing; the
pulpit says he was thinking about it all the time. When exas-
perated men rise up and sweep away an age-long tyranny and set
a nation free, the first thing the delighted pulpit does is to ad-
vertise it as God's work, and invite the people to get down on
their knees and pour out their thanks to him for it. And the
pulpit says with admiring emotion, "Let tyrants understand
that the Eye that never sleeps is upon them; and let them remember that the Lord our God will not always be patient, but
will loose the whirlwinds of his wrath upon them in his appointed day."

They forget to mention that he is the slowest mover in the
universe; that his Eye that never sleeps, might as well, since it
takes it a century to see what any other eye would see in a
week; that in all history there is not an instance where he
thought of a noble deed first, but always thought of it just
a little after somebody else had thought of it and done it. He
arrives then, and annexes the dividend.

Very well, six thousand years ago Shem was full of hookworms. Microscopic in size, invisible to the unaided eye. All of
the Creator's specially deadly disease-producers are invisible. It
is an ingenious idea. For thousands of years it kept man from
getting at the roots of his maladies, and defeated his attempts
to master them. It is only very recently that science has succeeded in exposing some of these treacheries.

The very latest of these blessed triumphs of science is the discovery and identification of the ambuscaded assassin which goes by the name of the hookworm. Its special prey is the bare-footed poor. It lies in wait in warm regions and sandy places and digs its way into their unprotected feet.

The hookworm was discovered two or three years ago by a physician, who had been patiently studying its victims for a long time. The disease induced by the hookworm had been do-ing its evil work here and there in the earth ever since Shem landed on Ararat, but it was never suspected to be a disease at all. The people who had it were merely supposed to be lazy, and were therefore despised and made fun of, when they should have been pitied. The hookworm is a peculiarly sneak-ing and underhand invention, and has done its surreptitious work unmolested for ages; but that physician and his helpers will exterminate it now.

God is back of this. He has been thinking about it for six thousand years, and making up his mind. The idea of exter-minating the hookworm was his. He came very near doing it before Dr. Charles Wardell Stiles did. But he is in time to get the credit of it. He always is.

It is going to cost a million dollars. He was probably just in the act of contributing that sum when a man pushed in ahead of him—as usual. Mr. Rockefeller. He furnishes the million, but the credit will go elsewhere—as usual. This morning's jour-nals tell us something about the hookworm's operations:

The hookworm parasites often so lower the vitality of those who are affected as to retard their physical and mental development, render them more susceptible to other diseases, make labor less effi-cient, and in the sections where the malady is most prevalent greatly increase the death rate from consumption, pneumonia, typhoid fever and malaria. It has been shown that the lowered vitality of multi-tudes, long attributed to malaria and climate and seriously affecting economic development, is in fact due in some districts to this para-site. The disease is by no means confined to any one class; it takes its toll of suffering and death from the highly intelligent and well to do as well as from the less fortunate. It is a conservative estimate that two millions of our people are affected by this parasite. The disease is more common and more serious in children of school age than in other persons.

Widespread and serious as the infection is, there is still a most encouraging outlook. The disease can be easily recognized, readily and effectively treated and by simple and proper sanitary precautions successfully prevented [with God's help].

The poor children are under the Eye that never sleeps, you see. They have had that ill luck in all the ages. They and "the Lord's poor"—as the sarcastic phrase goes—have never been able to get away from that Eye's attentions.

Yes, the poor, the humble, the ignorant—they are the ones that catch it. Take the "Sleeping Sickness," of Africa. This atrocious cruelty has for its victims a race of ignorant and un-offending blacks whom God placed in a remote wilderness, and bent his parental Eye upon them—the one that never sleeps when there is a chance to breed sorrow for somebody. He ar-ranged for these people before the Flood. The chosen agent was a fly, related to the tsetse; the tsetse is a fly which has com-mand of the Zambezi country and stings cattle and horses to death, thus rendering that region uninhabitable by man. The tsetse's awful relative deposits a microbe which produces the Sleeping Sickness. Ham was full of these microbes, and when the voyage was over he discharged them in Africa and the havoc began, never to find amelioration until six thousand years should go by and science should pry into the mystery and hunt out the cause of the disease. The pious nations are now thanking God, and praising him for coming to the rescue of his poor blacks. The pulpit says the praise is due to him. He is surely a curious Being. He commits a fearful crime, continues that crime unbroken for six thousand years, and is then en-titled to praise because he suggests to somebody else to modify its severities. He is called patient, and he certainly must be patient, or he would have sunk the pulpit in perdition ages ago for the ghastly compliments it pays him.

Science has this to say about the Sleeping Sickness, other-wise called the Negro Lethargy:

It is characterized by periods of sleep recurring at intervals. The disease lasts from four months to four years, and is always fatal. The victim appears at first languid, weak, pallid, and stupid. His eyelids become puffy, an eruption appears on his skin. He falls asleep while talking, eating, or working. As the disease progresses he is fed with difficulty and becomes much emaciated. The failure of nutrition and the appearance of bedsores are followed by convulsions and death. Some patients become insane.

It is he whom Church and people call Our Father in Heaven who has invented the fly and sent him to inflict this dreary long misery and melancholy and wretchedness, and decay of body and mind, upon a poor savage who has done the Great Crim-

inal no harm. There isn't a man in the world who doesn't pity
that poor black sufferer, and there isn't a man that wouldn't
make him whole if he could. To find the one person who has
no pity for him you must go to heaven; to find the one person
who is able to heal him and couldn't be persuaded to do it, you
must go to the same place. There is only one father cruel
enough to afflict his child with that horrible disease—only one.
Not all the eternities can produce another one. Do you like
reproachful poetical indignations warmly expressed? Here is
one, hot from the heart of a slave:

> Man's inhumanity to man
> Makes countless thousands mourn!

I will tell you a pleasant tale which has in it a touch of pathos. A man got religion, and asked the priest what he must do
to be worthy of his new estate. The priest said, "Imitate our
Father in Heaven, learn to be like him." The man studied his
Bible diligently and thoroughly and understandingly, and then
with prayers for heavenly guidance instituted his imitations. He
tricked his wife into falling downstairs, and she broke her back
and became a paralytic for life; he betrayed his brother into the
hands of a sharper, who robbed him of his all and landed him
in the almshouse; he inoculated one son with hookworms, another with the sleeping sickness, another with gonorrhea; he
furnished one daughter with scarlet fever and ushered her into
her teens deaf, dumb, and blind for life; and after helping a
rascal seduce the remaining one, he closed his doors against her
and she died in a brothel cursing him. Then he reported to the
priest, who said that *that* was no way to imitate his Father in
Heaven. The convert asked wherein he had failed, but the
priest changed the subject and inquired what kind of weather
he was having, up his way.

LETTER VIII

Man is without any doubt the most interesting fool there is.
Also the most eccentric. He hasn't a single written law, in his
Bible or out of it, which has any but just one purpose and
intention—to *limit* or *defeat* a law of God.

He can seldom take a plain fact and get any but a wrong
meaning out of it. He cannot help this; it is the way the con-

fusion he calls his mind is constructed. Consider the things he concedes, and the curious conclusions he draws from them.

For instance, he concedes that God made man. Made him without man's desire or privity.

This seems to plainly and indisputably make God, and God alone, responsible for man's acts. But man denies this.

He concedes that God has made angels perfect, without blemish, and immune from pain and death, and that he could have been similarly kind to man if he had wanted to, but denies that he was under any moral obligation to do it.

He concedes that man has no moral right to visit the child of his begetting with wanton cruelties, painful diseases and death, but refuses to limit God's privileges in this sort with the children of his begetting.

The Bible and man's statutes forbid murder, adultery, fornication, lying, treachery, robbery, oppression and other crimes, but contend that God is free of these laws and has a right to break them when he will.

He concedes that God gives to each man his temperament, his disposition, at birth; he concedes that man cannot by any process change this temperament, but must remain always under its dominion. Yet if it be full of dreadful passions, in one man's case, and barren of them in another man's, it is right and rational to punish the one for his crimes, and reward the other for abstaining from crime.

There—let us consider these curiosities.

Temperament (Disposition)

Take two extremes of temperament—the goat and the tortoise.

Neither of these creatures makes its own temperament, but is born with it, like man, and can no more change it than can man.

Temperament is the law of God written in the heart of every creature by God's own hand, and must be obeyed, and will be obeyed in spite of all restricting or forbidding statutes, let them emanate whence they may.

Very well, lust is the dominant feature of the goat's temperament, the law of God in its heart, and it must obey it and will obey it the whole day long in the rutting season, without stopping to eat or drink. If the Bible said to the goat, "Thou shalt not fornicate, thou shalt not commit adultery," even Man—sap-headed man—would recognize the fooolishness of the prohibition, and would grant that the goat ought not to be punished for obeying the law of his Maker. Yet he thinks it right and just that man should be put under the prohibition. All men. All alike.

On its face this is stupid, for, by temperament, which is the *real* law of God, many men are goats and can't help committing adultery when they get a chance; whereas there are numbers of men who, by temperament, can keep their purity and let an opportunity go by if the woman lacks in attractiveness. But the Bible doesn't allow adultery at all, whether a person can help it or not. It allows no distinction between goat and tortoise—the excitable goat, the emotional goat, that has to have some adultery every day or fade and die; and the tortoise, that cold calm puritan, that takes a treat only once in two years and then goes to sleep in the midst of it and doesn't wake up for sixty days. No lady goat is safe from criminal assault, even on the Sabbath Day, when there is a gentleman goat within three miles to leeward of her and nothing in the way but a fence fourteen feet high, whereas neither the gentleman tortoise nor the lady tortoise is ever hungry enough for the solemn joys of fornication to be willing to break the Sabbath to get them. Now according to man's curious reasoning, the goat has earned punishment, and the tortoise praise.

"Thou shalt not commit adultery" is a command which makes no distinction between the following persons. They are all required to obey it:

Children at birth.
Children in the cradle.
School children.
Youths and maidens.
Fresh adults.
Older ones.
Men and women of 40.
Of 50.
Of 60.
Of 70.
Of 80.
Of 90.
Of 100.

The command does not distribute its burden equally, and cannot.

It is not hard upon the three sets of children.

It is hard—harder—still harder upon the next three sets—cruelly hard.

It is blessedly softened to the next three sets.

It has now done all the damage it can, and might as well be put out of commission. Yet with comical imbecility it is continued, and the four remaining estates are put under its crushing ban. Poor old wrecks, they couldn't disobey if they tried. And think—because they holily refrain from adulterating each other, they get praise for it! Which is nonsense; for even the Bible knows enough to know that if the oldest veteran there could get his lost heyday back again for an hour he would cast that commandment to the winds and ruin the first woman he came across, even though she were an entire stranger.

It is as I have said: every statute in the Bible and in the law-books is an attempt to defeat a law of God—in other words an unalterable and indestructible law of nature. These people's God has shown them by a million acts that he respects none of the Bible's statutes. He breaks every one of them himself, adultery and all.

The law of God, as quite plainly expressed in woman's construction, is this: There shall be no limit put upon your intercourse with the other sex sexually, at any time of life.

The law of God, as quite plainly expressed in man's construction, is this: During your entire life you shall be under inflexible limits and restrictions, sexually.

During twenty-three days in every month (in the absence of pregnancy) from the time a woman is seven years old till she dies of old age, she is ready for action, and competent. As competent as the candlestick is to receive the candle. Competent every day, competent every night. Also, she wants that candle—yearns for it, longs for it, hankers after it, as commanded by the law of God in her heart.

But man is only briefly competent; and only then in the moderate measure applicable to the word in his sex's case. He is competent from the age of sixteen or seventeen thenceforward for thirty-five years. After fifty his performance is of poor quality, the intervals between are wide, and its satisfactions of no great value to either party; whereas his great-grandmother is as good as new. There is nothing the matter with her plant. Her candlestick is as firm as ever, whereas his candle is increasingly softened and weakened by the weather of age, as the years go by, until at last it can no longer stand, and is mournfully laid to rest in the hope of a blessed resurrection which is never to come.

By the woman's make, her plant has to be out of service

three days in the month and during a part of her pregnancy. These are times of discomfort, often of suffering. For fair and just compensation she has the high privilege of unlimited adultery all the other days of her life.

That is the law of God, as revealed in her make. What becomes of this high privilege? Does she live in the free enjoyment of it? No. Nowhere in the whole world. She is robbed of it everywhere. Who does this? Man. Man's statutes—if the Bible is the Word of God.

Now there you have a sample of man's "reasoning powers," as he calls them. He observes certain facts. For instance, that in all his life he never sees the day that he can satisfy one woman; also, that no woman ever sees the day that she can't overwork, and defeat, and put out of commission any ten masculine plants that can be put to bed to her.* He puts those strikingly suggestive and luminous facts together, and from them draws this astonishing conclusion: The Creator intended the woman to be restricted to one man.

So he concretes that singular conclusion into a law, for good and all.

And he does it without consulting the woman, although she has a thousand times more at stake in the matter than he has. His procreative competency is limited to an average of a hundred exercises per year for fifty years, hers is good for three thousand a year for that whole time—and as many years longer as she may live. Thus his life interest in the matter is five thousand refreshments, while hers is a hundred and fifty thousand; yet instead of fairly and honorably leaving the making of the law to the person who has an overwhelming interest at stake in it, this immeasurable hog, who has nothing at stake in it worth considering, makes it himself!

You have heretofore found out, by my teachings, that man is a fool; you are now aware that woman is a damned fool.

Now if you or any other really intelligent person were arranging the fairnesses and justices between man and woman, you would give the man a one-fiftieth interest in one woman,

* In the Sandwich Islands in 1866 a buxom royal princess died. Occupying a place of distinguished honor at her funeral were thirty-six splendidly built young native men. In a laudatory song which celebrated the various merits, achievements and accomplishments of the late princess those thirty-six stallions were called her *harem*, and the song said it had been her pride and boast that she kept the whole of them busy, and that several times it had happened that more than one of them had been able to charge overtime. [M. T.]

and the woman a harem. Now wouldn't you? Necessarily. I give you my word, this creature with the decrepit candle has arranged it exactly the other way. Solomon, who was one of the Deity's favorites, had a copulation cabinet composed of seven hundred wives and three hundred concubines. To save his life he could not have kept two of those young creatures satisfactorily refreshed, even if he had had fifteen experts to help him. Necessarily almost the entire thousand had to go hungry years and years on a stretch. Conceive of a man hardhearted enough to look daily upon all that suffering and not be moved to mitigate it. He even wantonly added a sharp pang to that pathetic misery; for he kept within those women's sight, always, stalwart watchmen whose splendid masculine forms made the poor lassies' mouths water but who hadn't anything to solace a candlestick with, these gentry being eunuchs. A eunuch is a person whose candle has been put out. By art.*

From time to time, as I go along, I will take up a Biblical statute and show you that it always violates a law of God, and then is imported into the lawbooks of the nations, where it continues its violations. But those things will keep; there is no hurry.

LETTER IX

The Ark continued its voyage, drifting around here and there and yonder, compassless and uncontrolled, the sport of the random winds and the swirling currents. And the rain, the rain, the rain! It kept on falling, pouring, drenching, flooding. No such rain had ever been seen before. Sixteen inches a day had been heard of, but that was nothing to this. This was a hundred and twenty inches a day—ten feet! At this incredible rate it rained forty days and forty nights, and submerged every hill that was four hundred feet high. Then the heavens and even the angels went dry; no more water was to be had.

As a Universal Flood it was a disappointment, but there had been heaps of Universal Floods before, as is witnessed by all the Bibles of all the nations, and this was as good as the best one.

* I purpose publishing these Letters here in the world before I return to you. Two editions. One, unedited, for Bible readers and their children; the other, expurgated, for persons of refinement. [M. T.]

At last the Ark soared aloft and came to a rest on the top of Mount Ararat, seventeen thousand feet above the valley, and its living freight got out and went down the mountain.

Noah planted a vineyard, and drank of the wine and was overcome.

This person had been selected from all the populations because he was the best sample there was. He was to start the human race on a new basis. This was the new basis. The promise was bad. To go further with the experiment was to run a great and most unwise risk. Now was the time to do with these people what had been so judiciously done with the others—drown them. Anybody but the Creator would have seen this. But he didn't see it. That is, maybe he didn't.

It is claimed that from the beginning of time he foresaw everything that would happen in the world. If that is true, he foresaw that Adam and Eve would eat the apple; that their posterity would be unendurable and have to be drowned; that Noah's posterity would in their turn be unendurable, and that by and by he would have to leave his throne in heaven and come down and be crucified to save that same tiresome human race again. The whole of it? No! A part of it? Yes. How much of it? In each generation, for hundreds and hundreds of generations, a billion would die and all go to perdition except perhaps ten thousand out of the billion. The ten thousand would have to come from the little body of Christians, and only one in the hundred of that little body would stand any chance. None of them at all except such Roman Catholics as should have the luck to have a priest handy to sandpaper their souls at the last gasp, and here and there a Presbyterian. No others savable. All the others damned. By the million.

Shall you grant that he foresaw all this? The pulpit grants it. It is the same as granting that in the matter of intellect the Deity is the Head Pauper of the Universe, and that in the matter of morals and character he is away down on the level of David.

LETTER X

The two Testaments are interesting, each in its own way. The Old one gives us a picture of these people's Deity as he was before he got religion, the other cne gives us a picture of him as he appeared afterward. The Old Testament is interested mainly in blood and sensuality. The New one in Salvation. Salvation by fire.

The first time the Deity came down to earth, he brought life and death; when he came the second time, he brought hell.

Life was not a valuable gift, but death was. Life was a fever-dream made up of joys embittered by sorrows, pleasure poisoned by pain; a dream that was a nightmare-confusion of spasmodic and fleeting delights, ecstasies, exultations, happinesses, interspersed with long-drawn miseries, griefs, perils, horrors, disappointments, defeats, humiliations, and despairs —the heaviest curse devisable by divine ingenuity; but death was sweet, death was gentle, death was kind; death healed the bruised spirit and the broken heart, and gave them rest and forgetfulness; death was man's best friend; when man could endure life no longer, death came and set him free.

In time, the Deity perceived that death was a mistake; a mistake, in that it was insufficient; insufficient, for the reason that while it was an admirable agent for the inflicting of misery upon the survivor, it allowed the dead person himself to escape from all further persecution in the blessed refuge of the grave. This was not satisfactory. A way must be contrived to pursue the dead beyond the tomb.

The Deity pondered this matter during four thousand years unsuccessfully, but as soon as he came down to earth and became a Christian his mind cleared and he knew what to do. He invented hell, and proclaimed it.

Now here is a curious thing. It is believed by everybody that while he was in heaven he was stern, hard, resentful, jealous, and cruel; but that when he came down to earth and assumed the name Jesus Christ, he became the opposite of what he was before: that is to say, he became sweet, and gentle, merciful, forgiving, and all harshness disappeared from his nature and a deep and yearning love for his poor human children took its place. Whereas it was as Jesus Christ that he devised hell and proclaimed it!

Which is to say, that as the meek and gentle Savior he was a thousand billion times crueler than ever he was in the Old Testament—oh, incomparably more atrocious than ever he was when he was at the very worst in those old days!

Meek and gentle? By and by we will examine this popular sarcasm by the light of the hell which he invented.

While it is true that the palm for malignity must be

granted to Jesus, the inventor of hell, he was hard and ungentle enough for all godlike purposes even before he became a Christian. It does not appear that he ever stopped to reflect that *he* was to blame when a man went wrong, inasmuch as the man was merely acting in accordance with the disposition he had afflicted him with. No, he punished the man, instead of punishing himself. Moreover the punishment usually over-sized the offense. Often, too, it fell, not upon the doer of a misdeed, but upon somebody else—a chief man, the head of a community, for instance.

And Israel abode in Shittim, and the people began to commit whoredom with the daughters of Moab.

And the Lord said unto Moses, Take *all the heads of the people*, and hang them up before the Lord against the Sun, that the fierce anger of the Lord may be turned away from Israel.

Does that look fair to you? It does not appear that the "heads of the people" got any of the adultery, yet it is they that are hanged, instead of "the people."

If it was fair and right in that day it would be fair and right today, for the pulpit maintains that God's justice is eternal and unchangeable; also that he is the Fountain of Morals, and that his morals are eternal and unchangeable. Very well, then, we must believe that if the people of New York should begin to commit whoredom with the daughters of New Jersey, it would be fair and right to set up a gallows in front of the city hall and hang the mayor and the sheriff and the judges and the archbishop on it, although they did not get any of it. It does not look right to me.

Moreover, you may be quite sure of one thing: it couldn't happen. These people would not allow it. They are better than their Bible. *Nothing* would happen here, except some lawsuits, for damages, if the incident couldn't be hushed up; and even down South they would not proceed against persons who did not get any of it; they would get a rope and hunt for the correspondents, and if they couldn't find them they would lynch a nigger.

Things have greatly improved since the Almighty's time, let the pulpit say what it may.

Will you examine the Deity's morals and disposition and conduct a little further? And will you remember that in the Sunday school the little children are urged to love the

Almighty, and honor him, and praise him, and make him their model and try to be as like him as they can? Read:

1 And the Lord spake unto Moses, saying,

2 Avenge the children of Israel of the Midianites: afterward shalt thou be gathered unto thy people. . . .

7 And they warred against the Midianites, as the Lord commanded Moses; and they slew all the males.

8 And they slew the kings of Midian, beside the rest of them that were slain; namely, Evi, and Rekem, and Zur, and Hur, and Reba, five kings of Midian: Balaam also the son of Beor they slew with the sword.

9 And the children of Israel took all the women of Midian captives and their little ones, and took the spoil of all their cattle, and all their flocks, and all their goods.

10 And they burnt all their cities wherein they dwelt, and all their goodly castles, with fire.

11 And they took all the spoil, and all the prey, both of men and of beasts.

12 And they brought the captives, and the prey, and the spoil unto Moses and Eleazar the priest, and unto the congregation of the children of Israel, unto the camp at the plains of Moab, which are by Jordan near Jericho.

13 And Moses, and Eleazar the priest, and all the princes of the congregation, went forth to meet them without the camp.

14 And Moses was wroth with the officers of the host, with the captains over thousands, and captains over hundreds, which came from the battle.

15 And Moses said unto them, Have ye saved all the women alive?

16 Behold, these caused the children of Israel, through the counsel of Balaam, to commit trespass against the Lord in the matter of Peor, and there was a plague among the congregation of the Lord.

17 Now therefore kill every male among the little ones, and kill every woman that hath known man by lying with him.

18 But all the woman children, that have not known a man by lying with him, keep alive for yourselves.

19 And do ye abide without the camp seven days: whosoever hath killed any person, and whosoever hath touched any slain, purify both yourselves and your captives on the third day, and on the seventh day.

20 And purify all your raiment, and all that is made of skins, and all work of goats' hair, and all things made of wood.

21 And Eleazar the priest said unto the men of war which went to the battle, This is the ordinance of the law which the Lord commanded Moses. . . .

25 And the Lord spake unto Moses, saying,

26 Take the sum of the prey that was taken, both of man and of

beast, thou, and Eleazar the priest, and the chief fathers of the congregation:

27 And divide the prey into two parts; between them that took the war upon them, who went out to battle, and between all the congregation:

28 And levy a tribute unto the Lord of the men of war which went out to battle. . . .

31 And Moses and Eleazar the priest did as the Lord commanded Moses.

32 And the booty, being the rest of the prey which the men of war had caught, was six hundred thousand, and seventy thousand and five thousand sheep,

33 And threescore and twelve thousand beeves,

34 And threescore and one thousand asses,

35 And thirty and two thousand persons in all, of women that had not known man by lying with him. . . .

40 And the persons were sixteen thousand; of which the Lord's tribute was thirty and two persons.

41 And Moses gave the tribute, which was the Lord's heave offering, unto Eleazar the priest, as the Lord commanded Moses. . . .

47 Even of the children of Israel's half, Moses took one portion of fifty, both of man and of beast, and gave them unto the Levites, which kept the charge of the tabernacle of the Lord; as the Lord commanded Moses.

10 When thou comest nigh unto a city to fight against it, then proclaim peace unto it. . . .

13 And when the Lord thy God hath delivered it into thine hands, thous shalt smite every male thereof with the edge of the sword:

14 But the women, and the little ones, and the cattle, and all that is in the city, even all the spoil thereof, shalt thou take unto thyself; and thou shalt eat the spoil of thine enemies, which the Lord thy God hath given thee.

15 Thus shalt thou do unto all the cities which are very far off from thee, which are not of the cities of these nations.

16 But of the cities of these people, which the Lord thy God doth give thee for an inheritance, thou shalt save alive nothing that breatheth.

The Biblical law says: "Thou shalt not kill."

The law of God, planted in the heart of man at his birth, says: "Thou shalt kill."

The chapter I have quoted shows you that the book-statute is once more a failure. It cannot set aside the more powerful law of nature.

According to the belief of these people, it was God himself who said: "Thou shalt not kill."

Then it is plain that he cannot keep his own commandments.

He killed all those people—every male.

They had offended the Deity in some way. We know what the offense was, without looking; that is to say, we know it was a trifle; some small thing that no one but a god would attach any importance to. It is more than likely that a Midianite had been duplicating the conduct of one Onan, who was commanded to "go in unto his brother's wife"—which he did; but instead of finishing, "he spilled it on the ground." The Lord slew Onan for that, for the Lord could never abide indelicacy. The Lord slew Onan, and to this day the Christian world cannot understand why he stopped with Onan, instead of slaying all the inhabitants for three hundred miles around— they being innocent of offense, and therefore the very ones he would usually slay. For that had always been his idea of fair dealing. If he had had a motto, it would have read, "Let no innocent person escape." You remember what he did in the time of the flood. There were multitudes and multitudes of tiny little children, and he knew they had never done him any harm; but their relations had, and that was enough for him: he saw the waters rise toward their screaming lips, he saw the wild terror in their eyes, he saw that agony of appeal in the mothers' faces which would have touched any heart but his, but he was after the guiltless particularly, and he drowned those poor little chaps.

And you will remember that in the case of Adam's posterity all the billions are innocent—none of them had a share in his offense, but the Deity holds them guilty to this day. None gets off, except by acknowledging that guilt—no cheaper lie will answer.

Some Midianite must have repeated Onan's act, and brought that dire disaster upon his nation. If that was not the indelicacy that outraged the feelings of the Deity, then I know what it was: some Midianite had been pissing against the wall. I am sure of it, for that was an impropriety which the Source of all Etiquette never could stand. A person could piss against a tree, he could piss on his mother, he could piss on his own breeches, and get off, but he must not piss against the wall— that would be going quite too far. The origin of the divine prejudice against this humble crime is not stated; but we know that the prejudice was very strong—so strong that nothing but a wholesale massacre of the people inhabiting the region where the wall was defiled could satisfy the Deity.

Take the case of Jeroboam. "I will cut off from Jeroboam him that pisseth against the wall." It was done. And not only was the man that did it cut off, but everybody else.

The same with the house of Baasha: everybody was exterminated, kinsfolks, friends, and all, leaving "not one that pisseth against a wall."

In the case of Jeroboam you have a striking instance of the Deity's custom of not limiting his punishments to the guilty; the innocent are included. Even the "remnant" of that unhappy house was removed, even "as a man taketh away dung, till it be all gone." That includes the women, the young maids, and the little girls. All innocent, for they couldn't piss against a wall. Nobody of that sex can. None but members of the other sex can achieve that feat.

A curious prejudice. And it still exists. Protestant parents still keep the Bible handy in the house, so that the children can study it, and one of the first things the little boys and girls learn is to be righteous and holy and not piss against the wall. They study those passages more than they study any others, except those which incite to masturbation. Those they hunt out and study in private. No Protestant child exists who does not masturbate. That art is the earliest accomplishment his religion confers upon him. Also the earliest her religion confers upon her.

The Bible has this advantage over all other books that teach refinement and good manners: that it goes to the child. It goes to the mind at its most impressible and receptive age—the others have to wait.

Thou shalt have a paddle upon thy weapon; and it shall be, when thou wilt ease thyself abroad, thou shalt dig therewith, and shalt turn back and cover that which cometh from thee.

That rule was made in the old days because "The Lord thy God walketh in the midst of thy camp."

It is probably not worthwhile to try to find out, for certain, why the Midianites were exterminated. We can only be sure that it was for no large offense; for the cases of Adam, and the Flood, and the defilers of the wall teach us that much. A Midianite may have left his paddle at home and thus brought on the trouble. However, it is no matter. The main thing is the trouble itself, and the morals of one kind and another that it offers for the instruction and elevation of the Christian of today.

God wrote upon the tables of stone: "Thou shalt not kill." Also: "Thou shalt not commit adultery."

Paul, speaking by the divine voice, advised against sexual intercourse *altogether*. A great change from the divine view as it existed at the time of the Midianite incident.

LETTER XI

Human history in all ages is red with blood, and bitter with hate, and stained with cruelties; but not since Biblical times have these features been without a limit of some kind. Even the Church, which is credited with having spilt more innocent blood, since the beginning of its supremacy, than all the political wars put together have spilt, has observed a limit. A sort of limit. But you notice that when the Lord God of Heaven and Earth, adored Father of Man, goes to war, there is no limit. He is totally without mercy—he, who is called the Fountain of Mercy. He slays, slays, slays! All the men, all the beasts, all the boys, all the babies; also all the women and all the girls, except those that have not been deflowered.

He makes no distinction between innocent and guilty. The babies were innocent, the beasts were innocent, many of the men, many of the women, many of the boys, many of the girls were innocent, yet they had to suffer with the guilty. What the insane Father required was blood and misery; he was indifferent as to who furnished it.

The heaviest punishment of all was meted out to persons who could not by any possibility have deserved so horrible a fate—the 32,000 virgins. Their naked privacies were probed, to make sure that they still possessed the hymen unruptured; after this humiliation they were sent away from the land that had been their home, to be sold into slavery; the worst of slaveries and the shamefulest, the slavery of prostitution; bed-slavery, to excite lust, and satisfy it with their bodies; slavery to any buyer, be he gentleman or be he a coarse and filthy ruffian.

It was the Father that inflicted this ferocious and unde-served punishment upon those bereaved and friendless virgins, whose parents and kindred he had slaughtered before their eyes. And were they praying to him for pity and rescue, meantime? Without a doubt of it.

These virgins were "spoil," plunder, booty. He claimed his share and got it. What use had *he* for virgins? Examine his later history and you will know.

His priests got a share of the virgins, too. What use could priests make of virgins? The private history of the Roman Catholic confessional can answer that question for you. The confessional's chief amusement has been seduction—in all the ages of the Church. Père Hyacinth testifies that of a hundred priests confessed by him, ninety-nine had used the confessional effectively for the seduction of married women and young girls. One priest confessed that of nine hundred girls and women whom he had served as father confessor in his time, none had escaped his lecherous embrace but the elderly and the homely. The official list of questions which the priest is required to ask will overmasteringly excite any woman who is not a paralytic.

There is nothing in either savage or civilized history that is more utterly complete, more remorselessly sweeping than the Father of Mercy's campaign among the Midianites. The official report does not furnish incidents, episodes, and minor details, it deals only in information in masses: all the virgins, all the men, all the babies, all "creatures that breathe," all houses, all cities; it gives you just one vast picture, spread abroad here and there and yonder, as far as eye can reach, of charred ruin and storm-swept desolation; your imagination adds a brooding stillness, an awful hush—the hush of death. But of course there were incidents. Where shall we get them?

Out of history of yesterday's date. Out of history made by the red Indian of America. He has duplicated God's work, and done it in the very spirit of God. In 1862 the Indians in Minnesota, having been deeply wronged and treacherously treated by the government of the United States, rose against the white settlers and massacred them; massacred all they could lay their hands upon, sparing neither age nor sex. Consider this incident:

Twelve Indians broke into a farmhouse at daybreak and captured the family. It consisted of the farmer and his wife and four daughters, the youngest aged fourteen and the eldest eighteen. They crucified the parents; that is to say, they stood them stark naked against the wall of the living room and nailed their hands to the wall. Then they stripped the daughters bare, stretched them upon the floor in front of their parents, and repeatedly ravished them. Finally they crucified the girls against the wall opposite the parents, and cut off their noses and their breasts. They also—but I will not go into that. There is a limit. There are indignities so atrocious that the pen cannot write them. One member of that poor crucified family —the father—was still alive when help came two days later.

Now you have one incident of the Minnesota massacre. I could give you fifty. They would cover all the different kinds of cruelty the brutal human talent has ever invented.

And now you know, by these sure indications, what happened under the personal direction of the Father of Mercies in his Midianite campaign. The Minnesota campaign was merely a duplicate of the Midianite raid. Nothing happened in the one that did not happen in the other.

No, that is not strictly true. The Indian was more merciful than was the Father of Mercies. He sold no virgins into slavery to minister to the lusts of the murderers of their kindred while their sad lives might last; he raped them, then charitably made their subsequent sufferings brief, ending them with the precious gift of death. He burned some of the houses, but not all of them. He carried out innocent dumb brutes, but he took the lives of none.

Would you expect this same conscienceless God, this moral bankrupt, to become a teacher of morals; of gentleness; of meekness; of righteousness; of purity? It looks impossible, extravagant; but listen to him. These are his own words:

Blessed are the poor in spirit, for theirs is the kingdom of heaven.
Blessed are they that mourn, for they shall be comforted.
Blessed are the meek, for they shall inherit the earth.
Blessed are they which do hunger and thirst after righteousness, for they shall be filled.
Blessed are the merciful, for they shall obtain mercy.
Blessed are the pure in heart, for they shall see God.
Blessed are the peace-makers, for they shall be called the children of God.
Blessed are they which are persecuted for righteousness' sake, for theirs is the kingdom of heaven.
Blessed are ye when men shall revile you and persecute you, and say all manner of evil against you falsely for my sake.

The mouth that uttered these immense sarcasms, these giant hypocrisies, is the very same that ordered the wholesale massacre of the Midianitish men and babies and cattle; the wholesale destruction of house and city; the wholesale banishment of the virgins into a filthy and unspeakable slavery. This is the same person who brought upon the Midianites the fiendish cruelties which were repeated by the red Indians, detail by detail, in Minnesota eighteen centuries later. The Midianite episode filled him with joy. So did the Minnesota one, or he would have prevented it.

The Beatitudes and the quoted chapters from Numbers and Deuteronomy ought always to be read from the pulpit together; then the congregation would get an all-round view of Our Father in Heaven. Yet not in a single instance have I ever known a clergyman to do this.

Papers of the Adam Family

I EXTRACT FROM METHUSELAH'S DIARY

The items here brought together were translated from the Adamic at different times but approximately in the sequence I have given them. In an unpublished philosophical work dated a thousand years after his death Mark Twain refers to himself under two titles, Bishop of New Jersey and Father of History. Both as a theologian and as a historian he had a lifelong interest in the private archives of the oldest human family. He nowhere tells us how or when the Adam family papers came into his possession, but his first translation from them appears to have been the two extracts from Methuselah's diary. I cannot date it exactly but it apparently belongs to the 1870's; that is, it precedes the translation and publication of Adam's Diary by at least fifteen years. A note of Albert B. Paine's says that he began with Shem's diary even earlier, in 1870, but if he did, the translation has been lost.

The translation from Methuselah belongs to a period when Mark was reading history systematically. He was preparing to write The Prince and the Pauper, and a sketch that was a by-product of his research has obviously influenced the style of this translation, which frequently reproduces the idiom of 1601. But, what is more important, he found in Tudor England and in the world before the Flood the recurrences and correspondences that he was later to generalize into a law of history. At the end of the first extract we encounter such a correspondence, one that probably stimulated him to translate this particular passage, the peace treaty with the Jabalites. He intended to pursue further the analogy with recent events in America. One of the summaries of passages in the archives which he read but did not translate (there are many such notes in the manuscripts) reads: "Take this up again under brief republican form of govt., when Methuselah is about 300 or 400 years old, and put in Custer and Howard and the Peace Commissioners and the Modoc Lava Beds and so forth and satirize freely." He had recognized a continuity from Adam's time, through the Tudors', to his own.

But a stronger reason for his choosing Methuselah's journals appears in an unobtrusive allusion in the second extract. Methuselah refers to "that silly deluge whereof overpious fools do prate and prophesy from time to time." The reader will find him still skeptical about it hundreds of years later, when Shem quotes his derision of the Ark. It was Methuselah's skepticism that attracted Mark—and his rebelliousness. Not altogether emancipated, he nevertheless perceived much stupidity, hypocrisy, and cruelty in the society to which he was born. His first diary shows his uneasiness about the institution of slavery, and notes on untranslated parts reveal that the uneasiness widened till he was ready to reject the entire religio-legal system of his people.

Methuselah had been influenced by the rising scientific spirit of his age, and a note shows that he became a freethinker. That phase belongs to the wild youth of his first century, to a period shortly after that of the two extracts, and it had an astonishing ending. When Shem's diary alludes to his having been disappointed in love at an early age, we are reminded of Zillah, the great-great-granddaughter of Methuselah's tutor Uz, who is tenderly mentioned in the translated passages. Further notes show that through love of Zillah he became an idolator, embracing her ancestral religion, the worship of Baal.

The notes show, moreover, that Methuselah could not quite dismiss as nonsense those "foolish prophecies about a flood." He recognized much true teaching in Judaism, inextricably mingled with superstition though it was, and he pondered it, pondering also the signs of the times. It seemed to him that the world was growing decadent and corrupt, as the prophets had foretold. If they had been right about the corruption of society, might they not also be right about its destruction? Methuselah wondered if his world might not be rushing toward disaster.

And with that we reach the core of Mark Twain's interest in him. What the Father of History saw in Methuselah's time was what he saw around him in the last quarter of the nineteenth century in America. Here was a correspondence, a repetition, an exemplification of the Mad Prophet's "Law of Periodical Repetition." In Methuselah's time as in Mark Twain's time, a great civilization had reached the point when the destructive forces it contained were beginning to dominate. He appreciated its greatness; he also appreciated the inevitability of its collapse. He and Methuselah lived in eras which they both loved and hated but in which they were never quite at home, eras with a doom on them, eras when the world was spinning toward the abyss.

For the fact that conditions all the Adam papers is that the Deluge is not far off. (The papers make clear that there is an error in the chronology of Genesis, which postdates the Flood by several centuries.) Mark's interest in the coming catastrophe was strong when he made the translations from Methuselah, in 1876 or 1877, but it was far stronger when, about 1906, his research reached the Mad Prophet. The year 920 After Creation was fateful for Adamic society —and he saw the same forces at work round him, the same softened people, the same corrupt plutocracy, the same venal and bewildered government, the same chaos. In the Mad Prophet, making his detached calculations on the very threshold of world catastrophe, he found a figure who, according to the Law of Periodical Repetition, might well be the Father of History himself.

B. DV.

The first day of the fourth month of the year 747 from the beginning of the world—This day am I sixty years old, I being born in the year 687 from the beginning of the world. Came certain of the family to me praying that I would marry, so that heirs fail not. I am but young to take upon me such cares, albeit I am minded that my father Enoch, my grandfather Jared, my great-grandfather Mahalaleel, and my great-great-grandfather Cainan did each and all take wives at an age like to that which I am now arrived at. All these have spoken their minds concerning me, and do concur in desiring that I marry, I being eldest son of my father and heir of this princely house in due succession, and ultimate possessor of the cities, principalities, and dignities unto it pertaining, when it shall please the gods to call hence those heirs and elder brethren that live and still stand between me and these high honors.

Tenth Day—Dismissed the several wise men and their servants with presents and sent them upon their way to their several countries, I not requiring tutors more, having finished my youth and stepped upon the threshold of manhood. With the sage Uz, that dwelleth in the far land of Nod, in that old city called Enoch, I did send a centurion and many stout men of war out of my own bodyguard, to protect him and his caravan from the children of Jabal that infest the desert places by the way. His great-great-granddaughter Zillah tarrieth yet in the house of their kinsman Habakkuk, she being content to extend her visit, and they to have her. A comely maid and modest.

Eighteenth Day—The anniversary of the building of the city—prosperity abide with Aumrath and all that dwell within her gates! My great-grandfather, Mahalaleel, that did lay the cornerstone three hundred years ago, sat in state in the high place of the temple and received the chiefs of the city, praising the greatness thereof, and the strength and power and the splendor of her belongings; saying he had seen the first house builded and watched the growth from that small beginning till this day that it covereth the five hills and the valleys be-

tween and possesseth a population that no man is able to
number. And indeed it is a goodly city, with temples and
palaces, strong walls, and streets that have no end, and not one
house but is stone. The house that was the first one is fallen
to ruin, but many visit it with reverence and none are allowed
to injure it, though many foolish persons, wanderers from
other parts, have the vain fashion of graving their names and
the obscure places whence they come, upon its stones, which
is silly and marketh the doer for a fool.

Twenty-fourth Day—This day performed before my father's
court certain mountebanks, whereof one did eat fire, placing
living coals within his mouth and crushing them with his teeth
and swallowing them; also drinking naphtha while it flamed,
yet betraying no inconvenience from it, but only relish and
content.

Then another, placing a child under a basket, drove a sword
down through it and drew it forth dripping blood, the child
shrieking meanwhile. The basket being turned, the child was
nowhere to be seen, nor yet its blood. But these be aged
tricks, and little worth.

One swallowed a crooked sword above an arm's length long.
This was a soft-spoken, gentle varlet, yet did I wish it might
rend his bowels and so end these entertainments since I nor any
might sit in my father's presence or depart whilst he remained.
But he was charmed, and marveled much; which comes of
holding himself in retirement and study and seeing little that
doth transpire abroad. Verily these threadbare vagaries did stir
his admiration to that degree that no louting clown new come
from out the country could surpass it.

Then went he to the theater in state, the court attending,
all in brave attire. This new actor, Luz, whose fame filleth the
land of late, so wrought upon the multitude in the great part
of Adam in the classic, venerable and noble play of the Driving
Forth from Eden (there being nothing comparable to it written in these modern times), that they wept aloud and many
times rose up shouting and so stood till it seemed they would
never give over. Yet in the midst cometh in Jebel, that never-
failing half-brother of my great-great-great-great-grandfather
Enos, and did raise his brows and turn him this way and that,
looking with compassion upon the people, as who should say,
"In sooth, call they *this* acting?" So always does he, being
never satisfied with anything except it be something ancient
and stupid which he hath seen and others have not; decrying

all that is modern as being trivial and weak, neither enjoying anything himself nor permitting others that would. Then discoursed he long and loud, with much inflated speech and pompous air, concerning what the stage had been in other times before this degenerate day; saying, "When the great Uzziel lived, lo, there was an Adam! Please God, when we that have seen true acting look back and remind us what the stage was four and five hundred years ago—" and then would he work himself up to such an anguish of grief and boasting and most hardy and prodigious lying, that one could be content he were back among his vanished idols and God be thanked that it was so. How tiresome these people be, soured and toothless and old, that go on living for no end, it seemeth, but to keep flinging in one's face the overrated marvels of an age that is forgot and that none regret but they themselves. Old age hath its charms, but this fashion is not of them. I had told him so, indeed, if such language might become my meager years and downy beard.

Twenty-seventh Day—This day, Zuar, a slave of mine, did prostrate himself before me, humbly reminding me that it is now six years since I bought him of his father. Calling my steward, he shewed me that it was so. Wherefore, the man being a Hebrew, I might not longer hold him, so told him he was free from bondage. Then bowed he again to the earth, saying, "My lord, I have a wife and children." Then would I, not thinking, have said, "Take them also," but that my steward, falling upon his knees, cried, "O Prince, I must not fail my duty, albeit it is hard: they came not with him when he was bought; your grace did give him his wife, and his children were born in servitude." Whereat I was troubled, as not knowing my own matter, I having no experience of a like case before, but said, "Well, if it be so, let it be so—give him money and clothing, and let him depart from his house alone; but be kind to his wife and babes, they shall not be sold, neither suffered to want."

Then Zuar rose up and, saluting, went out bowed as one that is stricken with a great sorrow. I was not easy in my mind, though fulfilling the law. I wished it might be otherwise. I went out to see, forbidding the guards to come, and found them locked in each other's arms, but not speaking, their faces turned to stone, and not a tear, the babes prattling about their knees, contending for a butterfly that one had caught. I drew back to my place, the pleasure of life gone out of me, which was strange, these being only slaves, dust under my feet. I must give this thing some further thought.

Twenty-eighth Day—Came these poor creatures to me, and Zuar, with a despondent face that belied his words, said, "My Lord, in the form and according to the usage of the law, I am come to declare that I love my lord, and my wife and my children, and do refuse to go out free; therefore, let my ear be bored with an awl before the judges, and I and mine by this token be returned to slavery forever, since that or even death itself is better than that I be parted from these that are more to me than bread and sunshine and the breath that giveth life."

I know not if I did right, but there was no finding it in my heart to suffer this; so I said, "It is a hard law and cruel; go forth free, all of ye, that my conscience may trouble me no more." These were servants of price, but I pray God I shall not repent me of it, since my state is so great and opulent it is but casting away a farthing in any wise.

Fifth Month, Third Day—I cannot abide the Princess Sarah, granddaughter of my kinsman Eliah, rich and great and old as that house is, nor will I marry her unless my father force me. Came she again, with a great train of nobles and lesser servants, three days since, to visit at my father's palace, which is over against my new one and no great space away. This girl is near my own age, though a trifle older, which is less pleasant than if she were a trifle younger, she being just turned sixty-one. But Lord, whilst at her age she should be blooming and gay, she apeth the gravity of a matron and hath a mature look and a dull complexion. She affects to be wise and learned, and goeth about with her nose in the air, lost in lofty contemplation. Pray God she hitch it not upon the bough of a tree and so hang herself, for it hath a hook that might serve for it. After the fashion of the time, she hath more hair upon her head that cometh from the bazaar than nature hath provided of her own to keep it company. It were as sensible to add to the proportions of the nose God's grace hath given us—then what, I marvel, would this woman do? Whithersoever she goeth, she draggeth a woolly and insufferable dog by a string and taketh it in her lap and comforteth it when she sits, and in chill weather covereth its body with a red embroidered cloth lest it be taken of a cold or a fever and the world mourn. Cursed be the day that I fall heir to its place and the affliction of the affections of its mistress. Amen.

Fifth Day—Came Zuar and his wife Mahlah, as I walked in

the Court of Fountains, and fell upon their faces before me to
make a petition; and when the guards would have dealt roughly
by them for intruding upon my privacy and my meditations, I
would not suffer it; for since I was lately merciful to these there
hath sprung up within me a consideration for them. Their petition being that I would attach them to my service, I did so,
albeit it was odd simplicity in creatures of their degree to prefer
a prayer in person to one of my quality; and did appoint Mahlah to serve in the apartments of the women, and Zuar to be
near me and be Master of the Pages, with good wage for both,
whereat they were very grateful, not expecting or aspiring to
such high fortune.

About noon saw the girl Zillah pass by the great gate of the
palace, with but a single servant following, for these are people
of mere civilian degree and of no estate. Uz, her great-great-
grandfather, hath great learning, but cometh of ancestry of no
quality. They be idolaters, worshipers of Baal, and so suffer certain restraints and curtailments of privilege under the law. This
girl is very beautiful—more so, indeed, than I had before observed.

Tenth Day—All the whole city did flock to the streets, the
walls, the housetops and all places of vantage, to get sight of
the savages new come to town from the famous tribe of the
Jabalites, that live not in houses, but in tents, and wander in
lawless hordes through the length and breadth of the great
deserts in the far northeast that lie toward the land of Nod.
These came to the number of twenty, greater and lesser chiefs,
with many servants, all upon camels and dromedaries, with a
fantastic sort of barbaric pomp, to make submission to my
father and enter into a covenant of peace, they receiving goods
and trinkets and implements of husbandry, and undertaking to
make the right of way secure and not molest our caravans and
merchants. A visit like to this they make to us as often as once
in fifty or sixty years, and then go away and break the covenant
and make trouble again. But they are not always to blame.
They covenant to go and abide upon lands set apart for them,
and subsist by the arts of peace; but the agents sent out to gov-
ern them do cheat them and maltreat them, removing them to
other stations not so good and stealing from them their fertile
lands and hunting districts, and abusing them with blows
when they resist—a thing they will not abide; and so they rise
by night and slaughter all that fall into their hands, revenging
the agents' treachery and oppression as best they can. Then

go our armies forth to carry desolation to their hearthstones
but succeed not. These that came today went about the city
viewing the wonders of it, yet never exclaiming, nor betraying
admiration in any way. At the audience many loving speeches
were made upon both sides, and they were feasted and sent
away with store of presents, mainly implements of husbandry,
the which they will fashion into weapons and go out against
their persecutors again. They were a wild spectacle, and fierce
of countenance, a goodly show; but they and the other tribes
of their sort are a sore problem to my father and his council.
They worship no god; and if we in goodness of heart do send a
missionary to show them the way of life, they listen with
respect to all he hath to say, and then they eat him. This doth
tend to hinder the spread of light.

II   A LATER EXTRACT FROM
METHUSELAH'S DIARY

*It was Mark Twain's intention to translate in detail Methuselah's ob-
servations on manners and morals, on his travels in distant lands, and
on the recurrence of fashions and beliefs. He expected to give us an
account of an experiment in republicanism which occurred in the
middle period of Methuselah's life, the bureaucracy that grew up as a
result, and such accompaniments of it as a women's rights crusade, the
corruption of the judiciary, and the triumph of the demagogues. A
typical incident was summarized thus in his notes:* "Poor foreign
devils lost and starving in the desert. Republican govt. of Meth. can't
relieve or rescue them. Somebody observes that if you can pretend
they are robbers or other criminals govt. will hunt them up with
alacrity—which is done. Disgust of govt. to find they are honest and
harmless."*

*Methuselah met a number of eccentrics, notably one Lamech (not
to be confused with his son Lamech), who was a murderer and
"charmed with the idea that any man that shall avenge the murder
will have to suffer seventy-and-seven fold, if Cain's must suffer seven-
fold." There is also a notation that Methuselah once met Cain. He
was not able, however, to gratify his great desire to visit Eden. The
place was under a taboo, none could visit it, and centuries of mystery
about it had created terrible legends.*

*Methuselah observes the slight differences in the religions he en-
counters, and makes notes on the local dialects of the mother tongue.
He sees a census of the family of Seth or Enos:* "1200 brothers and
sisters mustered, inspected, counted, tallied, invoiced, account of
stock." *In his old age on a similar occasion he* "is introduced to

brothers and sisters never met before. Invites 40 or 50 to dine. Sees resemblance—have much family talk about What ever became of Jim?—Married So-and-so and moved into So-and-so 200 years ago, etc." (The problem here suggested grows acute in the Mad Prophet's time.)

Another note repeats a familiar theme. "Remains 20 years in Enoch (short stay—is hurried); returns there 500 years later—everybody married or dead or moved away—inquires for all—reads moldering monuments to them—asks after this and that one—is all very sad—so many changes—finally finds one withered wretch who was a humble youth and befriended him in the old time—shows him graves, ruined houses and tells everything. Changes in town's appearance and customs. Men kissing going out of fashion—been out twice before in M's time."

(The last two notes are out of key with the others and I suspect that they were made long after the two translations from Methuselah. The appearance of the manuscript supports the evidence of the content. They are on a different kind of paper, and the penmanship has changed from the large, cursive style of the seventies. It is much nearer the small, precise copperplate of the nineties. At a guess, these two notes were made in the late eighties and signify a brief reawakening of interest in Methuselah which Mark did not follow up.)

But neither Methuselah's travels nor his reflections on society are translated at length in the second extract. Instead, Mark is principally interested in the coming visit of Adam. A number of notes bear on the ceremonies and the Pageant of Progress that accompanied them. Apparently Methuselah was going to review the whole of Adamic culture. But the translation was dropped abruptly: I do not know why. I imagine that by this time the Father of History had got absorbed in the reign of Edward VI (he began writing The Prince and the Pauper in 1877) or in his own travels in Europe (1878) preparatory to writing A Tramp Abroad.

The second extract was translated, I think, very soon after the first. The date is almost certainly 1876, 1877, or 1878. My guess is that both date from the summer of 1876 and were written at Quarry Farm.

B. DV.

Tenth Day—It taketh but short space to craze men of indifferent understanding with a new thing. Behold, 'tis now but two years gone that a certain ancient game, played with a ball, hath come up again, yet already are all mouths filled with the phrases that describe its parts and movement; insomuch, indeed, that the ears of the sober and such as would busy themselves with weightier matters are racked with the clack of the same till they they do ache with anguish. If a man deceive his neighbor with a shrewd trick that doth advantage himself to his neighbor's hurt, the vulgar say of the sufferer that he was Caught out on a Foul. If one accomplisheth a great and sudden triumph of any sort soever, 'tis said of him that he hath Made a Three-Base Hit. If one fail utterly in an enterprise of pith and moment, you shall hear this said concerning him: "Hash-bat-kakolath."* Thus hath this vile deformity of speech entered with familiar insolence into the very warp and woof of the language, and made ugly that which before was shapely and beautiful. Today, by command of my father, was this game contested in the great court of his palace after the manner of the playing of it three centuries gone by. Nine men that had their calves clothed in red did strive against other nine that had blue hose upon their calves. Certain of those in blue stood at distances, one from another, stooping, each with his palms upon his knees, watching; these called they Basemen and Fielders—wherefore, God knoweth. It concerneth me not to know, neither to care. One with red legs stood wagging a club about his head, which from time to time he struck upon the ground, then wagged he it again. Behind him bent one with blue legs that did spit much upon his hands, and was called a Catcher. Beside him bent one called Umpire, clothed in the common fashion of the time, who marked upon the ground with a stick, yet accomplished nothing by it that I could make out. Saith this one, "Low Ball." Whereat one with blue legs did deliver a ball with vicious force straight at him that bore the club, but failed to bring him down, through some blemish of his aim. At once did all that are called Basemen and Fielders spit upon their hands and stoop and watch again. He that bore the club did suffer the ball to be flung at him divers times, but did always bend in his body or bend it out and so save himself, whilst the others spat upon their hands, he at the same instant endeavoring to destroy the Umpire with his bludgeon, yet not succeeding, through grievous awkwardness. But in the fullness of time was he more fortunate, and did lay the Umpire dead, which mightily pleased me, yet fell himself, he failing to avoid the ball, which this time cracked his skull, to my deep gratitude and satisfaction. Conceiving this to be the end, I did crave my father's leave to go, and got it, though all beside me did remain, to see the rest disabled. Yet had I seen a sufficiency, and shall visit this sport no more, forasmuch as the successful hits come too laggingly, wherefore the game doth lack excitement.

* This is not translatable into English, but it is about equivalent to "Lo, he is *whitewashed*."—THE EDITOR [M. T.]

Moreover was Jebel there, windy with scorn of these modern players, and boastful of certain mighty Nines he knew three hundred years gone by—dead now, and rotten, praise God, who doeth all things well.

Twelfth Day—The rumor that has been steadily gathering strength these twenty years, that the head of our princely house, the father of the nations of the earth, the most noble, most august and venerable ADAM, (on whom be peace!) willeth to visit my father in this his capital city, is rumor no more, but verity. The embassage approacheth with the tidings. Exceeding great is the tumult of the city for joy and thanksgiving. My father commandeth his chief minister to make due preparation.

Thirteenth Day—Came men of trust this day, that report the embassage as tarrying by the oasis Balka, eighteen days' journey hence, toward the south.

Fourteenth Day—There is no talk but of the great news and of the embassage. At the rising of the sun went my father's envoys forth in gorgeous state, to take the road, they bearing presents of gold and precious stones, spices and robes of honor. With banners and with sound of martial music went they, a glittering host, marching past until I wearied of the numbers and the noise. The multitudes that massed themselves upon the housetops or followed shouting were beyond the power of man to estimate. 'Tis a great day.

Fifteenth Day—My father hath commanded that the Palace of the Palms be new garnished for the ambassador that cometh, and his following. Eight hundred artisans and artists will set to work with all dispatch to paint and gild and renovate.

Sixteenth Day—To the museum, to see the raiments of fig leaves and of strange untanned skins of beasts our parents wore in Eden, in the olden time. Likewise the Flaming Sword the which the Angel bore. Now that the city is so wrought upon by the growing excitement, 'tis said the museum cannot accommodate more than some few thousands of the hosts that now daily clamor for admittance to the relics. That I might see as the simple see, and hear as the simple hear, and not be myself a show and plagued with the attentions due my state and dignity, went I disguised as a mere mohac,* not even clogged with a servant. Some hundreds of guides walked the prodigious

* Untranslatable. It means something better than a professional man, and not so good as an artist. Thus fine were the caste distinctions of the time.—THE EDITOR [M. T.]

ranges of apartments, with eager troops of people following, and made explanation of the gathered marvels. I perceived that these touched not upon their wares at random, but in rigid sequence, and that their speech by old habit had formed itself into an unchangeable sequence of words, hard, inflectionless, and void of all heart and expression as if a machine had made it. He whom I did follow had held his post four hundred years, clacking the same speech, day in, day out, through all that weary time, till now was he no more master of his jaws; once they set themselves awagging, only God could stop them before the speech was done. The foolish rhetoric and flourish of it, that once had had a sort of showy sound, mayhap, was now like to make one laugh for derision or cry for pity, so flat and lifeless was it. Poor old withered ass, thrice did I interrupt, to test him. 'Twas as I had conceived; it threw him out, and he was forced to go back and begin again at the beginning. It was on this wise: Saith he, "Lo, this dread weapon, grim memorial of that awful day; flaming with consuming fires that o'er the darkening fields of Eden cast their lurid ray——" I, interrupting, did inquire about a huge thing that bore the legend, The Similitude and Likeness of the Key of the Garden, the Original whereof lieth in the Treasure House of Cain in the far City of Enoch. The aged guide was sore troubled with this, and did try to answer me, but failing once and yet again, did then endeavour to find the place whereat he had late left off in his wretched speech; but not succeeding, went he back again and rasped out as formerly: "Lo, this dread weapon, grim memorial of that awful day; flaming with consuming fires that o'er the darkening fields of Eden cast their lurid ray——" I, interrupting yet twice again, each time returned he to his accursed "Lo, this dread weapon." Then suddenly being wroth, perceiving by signs of merriment among the crowd that he was being played upon, turned he upon me, saying, "Though I be of mean estate and lowly calling, it yet ill becometh one of but mohac degree and graceless youth to shame mine age with scorn." Being angered, I never having known insult before, I was near to saying, "By the law, whoso offends any of the royal house his head is forfeit." But I remembered myself in time and spake not, purposing at another season to have him crucified, together with his family.

I saw no curiosity that riveted the people's gaze like to the Fig Leaves. Yet are they not leaves, in truth, but only the skeletons thereof, instead, the fabric all decayed and gone save only

the ribs or veinings. There be cavilers that say we shall not lack
for the original garments of the Garden whilst fig trees grow
and beasts remain to renew these sacred treasures withal. As for
me, I say nothing, since that is most discreet. Yet am I pained
to remember that there exists at this day, in each of seven
cities, the Only True and Original Flaming Sword of Expul-
sion. This moveth one to doubt.

Presently came the sweet idolator by, and was swallowed up
and lost in the crowd. Straightway began I to dream and muse,
and so, losing zest for the marvels treasured about me, betook
me home.

Twentieth Day—God send that embassage come soon, else
cannot the people contain themselves. There is naught but talk
of this great thing, and preparation for it. Still, many days must
yet elapse before these expectations bring their fruit.

Twenty-seventh Day—Perish the generation of Jabal! Let
the hand wither that ceased not with contriving the noble or-
gan and the charming harp, but must shut up an unappeasable
devil in the bowels of a box, with privilege to vagrants to
grind anguish out of him with a crank and name it Music.
This new thing, being not yet a century invented, has yet
spread to all parts like to a pestilence; so that at this day in
every city shall you see vagabonds from strange lands grinding
these dread boxes, in the company and companionship of a
monkey. 'Twere endurable, were there variety in the Music;
but alack, they seem all to play but the one tune—the new
one that did come into favor some thirty years agone and seems
not like to go out again before the world shall drown in that
silly deluge whereof overpious fools with ill digestion do prate
and prophesy from time to time. 'Tis said the new excitement
hath increased our horde of grinders mightily, so that there
be in the city now full eighty thousand, which do all grind,
without ceasing, that one tearful ditty: "O, Kiss Haggag for
His Mother." Verily is this time waxing intolerable to me.
Though Haggag were damned, yet could I not be content, so
sore is my rage that he was ever born, since without him this
infliction had not come upon us.

Second Day of the Sixth Month of the Year 747—Yesterday
arrived my father's envoys, bringing the august embassage,
whom my father received in mighty state at the city gates. Vast
was the procession, and curious the garbs, and everything very
fine and noble to see. The city was mad with exultation. Nothing like to this noise and confusion have I seen before. Every

house and street and all the palaces were blazing with light all the night; and such as stood upon the distant eastward mountains said the city had the seeming of a far-off plain frosted thick with cut gems that glowed and winked with a bewitching soft radiance.

The ambassador hath delivered his tidings, and now there is not any more doubt. Adam indeed will come, the time is set: the year 787 cr the year that followeth it. Public proclamation was made and all the city is clamorous with delight. My father's orders have gone forth to set in train the preparations due to so majestic an event.

Now will begin the games and other pleasures meet for the entertainment of the ambassador, so my father has commanded public holiday during the two months which this must last.

III EXTRACT FROM EVE'S AUTO-BIOGRAPHY

Returning to the archives shortly after 1890, the translator determined to go back of Methuselah to their common ancestor, the founder of the damned human race. Readers of Mark Twain will remember his lifelong affection for Adam, his many allusions to him, his proposal to erect a monument to him, and other enterprises undertaken on his behalf. Always excepting Jehovah and Satan, Adam interested him more than any other character in Biblical society. At some time before March 22, 1893, he completed his translation of Adam's diary, which was first published in The Niagara Book (1893) and which, somewhat amended, is now a part of The $30,000 Bequest and Other Stories (1906).

In the summer of 1905 Mark made his translation of "Eve's Diary." It was first published as part of Their Husbands' Wives, a collection of novelettes edited by William Dean Howells and Henry M. Alden.

"Eve's Autobiography," which follows, is troublesome to the editor and seems to have been no less so to the translator. With this manuscript he encountered serious textual variants in the Adam papers. It is not surprising that traditions should become confused in the course of a thousand years, and there is less confusion in the private family archives than in the Book of Genesis. But the Father of History himself could not straighten out the three different accounts of Eden before the Fall that he found in the archives or determine which of them were apocryphal. No doubt legendary elements and copyists' errors have crept into all three, and Mark Twain's decision was that they do not matter. He recognized in "Eve's Diary," which he translated in 1905, an idyllic love story, a fragment whose place in the papers is similar to that of the Book of Ruth in the Old Testament. Possibly apocryphal and certainly without bearing on the historical processes whose exemplification in the papers had interested him thirty years before, it was nevertheless a charming bit of mythology and he published it as such.

He appears to have returned immediately to the archives and to have begun a research into the year 920 After Creation. On the way to it, perhaps as a background study, he translated part of the longest manuscript in the archives, "Eve's Autobiography." I omit part of the translation, about four thousand words at the beginning and about a hundred words where the manuscript abruptly breaks off. I leave out the first part not only because the account of Eve's earliest days with Adam contradicts the account in the "diaries" already published (as the foreshadowing of the Temptation is inconsistent with the fragments of Eve's diary and Satan's diary now published in Europe and Elsewhere) but also because stretches of it are dull and sentimental. The translator seems to have recognized that weakness—and he was, besides, principally interested in getting on toward Eve's last years, to the Great Society whose collapse is foreshadowed in the remaining papers.

Notes that summarize untranslated parts of her autobiography show that Eve understood what was happening to her people quite as clearly as the Mad Prophet did. In particular she intended to discuss the cyclical reappearance of a thaumaturgy which the Father of History identified as a form of Christian Science. The rise of such magic, she thought, signified the decline of genuine religious feeling and therefore the weakening of religious sanctions. It was evidence of decay and all through history it had been a forerunner of catastrophe. When men begin to preach such religions, civilization is dying and it is time for the Flood. This is only one of many cyclical phenomena which appear in intricate relationships when civilization is beginning to go down. The Mad Prophet was to summarize them very soon now.

The structure of the omitted portion of the autobiography can be made out from the part printed here. At some time after the year 900, Eve is looking back over the course of her life. Her narrative is interspersed with quotations from old diaries, and the part which I print becomes, halfway along, a single sustained quotation. Readers will perceive that her story is occasionally inconsistent with previously published versions of it, but there is no important contradiction. There is, however, one flagrant textual error, probably the translator's. On page 109 Eve speaks of Adam as already dead, whereas the next chapter makes clear that he was alive when she was writing.

The translation was abandoned, I believe, because of her leisureliness. After nine thousand words she had not yet got out of Eden—and Mark's interest was centered on events nearly a thousand years later than the Fall. (Note, however, in a later chapter, that the Mad

Prophet has read more of the "Autobiography" than Mark translated.)

This translation cannot be certainly dated. Paine gives it two dates, both unimpeachable: "1900's" and "about 1905." I believe that it is later than "Eve's Diary" (summer of 1905) and that it was written in the fall of 1905 or in 1906.

B. DV.

. . . Love, peace, comfort, measureless contentment—that was life in the Garden. It was a joy to be alive. Pain there was none, nor infirmity, nor any physical signs to mark the flight of time; disease, care, sorrow—one might feel these outside the pale, but not in Eden. There they had no place, there they never came. All days were alike, and all a dream of delight.

Interests were abundant; for we were children, and ignorant; ignorant beyond the conception of the present day. We knew nothing—nothing whatever. We were starting at the very bottom of things—at the very beginning; we had to learn the A B C of things. Today the child of four years knows things which we were still ignorant of at thirty. For we were children without nurses and without instructors. There was no one to tell us anything. There was no dictionary, and we could not know whether we used our words correctly or not; we liked large ones, and I know now that we often employed them for their sound and dignity, while quite ignorant of their meaning; and as to our spelling, it was a profligate scandal. But we cared not a straw for these trifles; so that we accumulated a large and showy vocabulary, we cared nothing for the means and the methods.

But studying, learning, inquiring into the cause and nature and purpose of everything we came across, were passions with us, and this research filled our days with brilliant and absorbing interest. Adam was by constitution and proclivity a scientist; I may justly say I was the same, and we loved to call ourselves by that great name. Each was ambitious to beat the other in scientific discovery, and this incentive added a spur to our friendly rivalry, and effectively protected us against falling into idle and unprofitable ways and frivolous pleasure-seeking.

Our first memorable scientific discovery was the law that water and like fluids run downhill, not up. It was Adam that found this out. Days and days he conducted his experiments secretly, saying nothing to me about it; for he wanted to make perfectly sure before he spoke. I knew something of prime importance was disturbing his great intellect, for his repose was troubled and he thrashed about in his sleep a good deal. But at last he was sure, and then he told me. I could not believe it, it seemed so strange, so impossible. My astonishment was his triumph, his reward. He took me from rill to rill—dozens of them—saying always, "There—you see it runs downhill—in every case it runs downhill, never up. My theory was right; it is proven, it is established, nothing can controvert it." And it was a pure delight to see his exultation in this great discovery.

In the present day no child wonders to see the water run down and not up, but it was an amazing thing then, and as hard to believe as any fact I have ever encountered. You see, that simple matter had been under my eyes from the day I was made, but I had never happened to notice it. It took me some time to accept it and adjust myself to it, and for a long time I could not see a running stream without voluntarily or involuntarily taking note of the dip of the surface, half expecting to see Adam's law violated; but at last I was convinced and remained so; and from that day forth I should have been startled and perplexed to see a waterfall going up the wrong way. Knowledge has to be acquired by hard work; none of it is flung at our heads gratis.

That law was Adam's first great contribution to science; and for more than two centuries it went by his name—Adam's Law of Fluidic Precipitation. Anybody could get on the soft side of him by dropping a casual compliment or two about it in his hearing. He was a good deal inflated—I will not try to conceal it—but not spoiled. Nothing ever spoiled him, he was so good and dear and right-hearted. He always put it by with a deprecating gesture, and said it was no great thing, some other scientist would have discovered it by and by; but all the same, if a visiting stranger had audience of him and was tactless enough to forget to mention it, it was noticeable that that stranger was not invited to call again. After a couple of centuries, the discovery of the law got into dispute, and was wrangled over by scientific bodies for as much as a century, the credit being finally given to a more recent person. It was a cruel blow. Adam was never the same man afterward. He carried that sorrow in his heart for six hundred years, and I have always believed that it shortened his life. Of course throughout his days he took precedence of kings and of all the race as First Man, and had the honors due to that great rank, but these distinctions could not compensate him for that lamented ravishment, for he was a true scientist and the First; and he confided to me, more than once, that if he could have kept the glory of Discoverer of the Law of Fluidic Precipitation he would have been content to pass as his own son and Second Man. I did what I could to comfort him. I said that as First Man his fame was secure; and that a time would come when the name of the pretended discoverer of the law that water runs downhill would fade and perish and be forgotten in the earth. And I believe that. I have never ceased to believe it. That day will surely come.

I scored the next great triumph for science myself: to wit, how the milk gets into the cow. Both of us had marveled over that mystery a long time. We had followed the cows around for years—that is, in the daytime—but had never caught them drinking a fluid of that color. And so, at last we said they undoubtedly procured it at night. Then we took turns and watched them by night. The result was the same—the puzzle remained unsolved. These proceedings were of a sort to be expected in beginners, but one perceives, now, that they were unscientific. A time came when experience had taught us better methods. One night as I lay musing, and looking at the stars, a grand idea flashed through my head, and I saw my way! My first impulse was to wake Adam and tell him, but I resisted it and kept my secret. I slept no wink the rest of the night. The moment the first pale streak of dawn appeared I flitted stealthily away; and deep in the woods I chose a small grassy spot and wattled it in, making a secure pen; then I enclosed a cow in it. I milked her dry, then left her there, a prisoner. There was nothing there to drink—she must get milk by her secret alchemy, or stay dry.

All day I was in a fidget, and could not talk connectedly I was so preoccupied; but Adam was busy trying to invent a multiplication table, and did not notice. Toward sunset he had got as far as 6 times 9 are 27, and while he was drunk with the joy of his achievement and dead to my presence and all things else, I stole away to my cow. My hand shook so with excitement and with dread failure that for some moments I could not get a grip on a teat; then I succeeded, and the milk came! Two gallons. Two gallons, and nothing to make it out of. I knew at once the explanation: *the milk was not taken in by the mouth, it was condensed from the atmosphere through the cow's hair.* I ran and told Adam, and his happiness was as great as mine, and his pride in me inexpressible.

Presently he said, "Do you know, you have not made merely

one weighty and far-reaching contribution to science, but two."

And that was true. By a series of experiments we had long ago arrived at the conclusion that atmospheric air consisted of water in invisible suspension; also, that the components of water were hydrogen and oxygen, in the proportion of two parts of the former to one of the latter, and expressible by the symbol H_2O. My discovery revealed the fact that there was still another ingredient—milk. We enlarged the symbol to H_2O,M.

INTERPOLATED EXTRACTS FROM "EVE'S DIARY"

Another discovery. One day I noticed that William McKinley was not looking well. He is the original first lion, and has been a pet of mine from the beginning. I examined him, to see what was the matter with him, and found that a cabbage which he had not chewed, had stuck in his throat. I was unable to pull it out, so I took the broomstick and rammed it home. This relieved him. In the course of my labors I had made him spread his jaws, so that I could look in, and I noticed that there was something peculiar about his teeth. I now subjected the teeth to careful and scientific examination, and the result was a consuming surprise: the lion is not a vegetarian, he is carnivorous, a flesh-eater! Intended for one, anyway.

I ran to Adam and told him, but of course he scoffed, saying, "Where would he find flesh?"

I had to grant that I didn't know.

"Very well, then, you see, yourself, that the idea is apocryphal. Flesh was not intended to be eaten, or it would have been provided. No flesh having been provided, it follows, of a necessity, that no carnivora have been intruded into the scheme of things. Is this a logical deduction, or isn't it?"

"It is."

"Is there a weak place in it anywhere?"

"No."

"Very well, then, what have you to say?"

"That there is something better than logic."

"Indeed? What is it?"

"Fact."

I called a lion, and made him open his mouth.

"Look at this larboard upper jaw," I said. "Isn't this long forward tooth a canine?"

He was astonished, and said impressively, "By my halidom it is!"

"What are these four, to rearward of it?"

"Premolars, or my reason totters!"

"What are these two at the back?"

"Molars, if I know a molar from a past participle when I see it. I have no more to say, Statistics cannot lie; this beast is not graminivorous."

He is always like that—never petty, never jealous, always just, always magnanimous; prove a thing to him and he yields at once and with a noble grace. I wonder if I am worthy of this marvelous boy, this beautiful creature, this generous spirit?

It was a week ago. We examined animal after animal, then, and found the estate rich in thitherto unsuspected carnivora. Somehow it is very affecting, now, to see a stately Bengal tiger stuffing himself with strawberries and onions; it seems so out of character, though I never felt so about it before.

[*Later*] Today, in a wood, we heard a Voice.

We hunted for it, but could not find it. Adam said he had heard it before, but had never seen it, though he had been quite close to it. So he was sure it was like the air, and could not be seen. I asked him to tell me all he knew about the Voice, but he knew very little. It was Lord of the Garden, he said, and had told him to dress the Garden and keep it; and it had said we must not eat of the fruit of a certain tree and that if we ate of it we should surely die. Our death would be certain. That was all he knew. I wanted to see the tree, so we had a pleasant long walk to where it stood alone in a secluded and lovely spot, and there we sat down and looked long at it with interest, and talked. Adam said it was the tree of knowledge of good and evil.

"Good and evil?"

"Yes."

"What is that?"

"What is what?"

"Why, those things. What is good?"

"I do not know. How should I know?"

"Well, then, what is evil?"

"I suppose it is the name of something, but I do not know what."

"But, Adam, you must have *some* idea of what it is."

"Why should I have some idea? I have never seen the thing,

how am I to form any conception of it? What is your own notion of it?"

Of course I had none, and it was unreasonable of me to require him to have one. There was no way for either of us to guess what it might be. It was a new word, like the other; we had not heard them before, and they meant nothing to us. My mind kept running on the matter, and presently I said, "Adam, there are those other new words—die, and death. What do they mean?"

"I have no idea."

"Well, then, what do you *think* they mean?"

"My child, cannot you see that it is impossible for me to make even a plausible guess concerning a matter about which I am absolutely ignorant? A person can't *think* when he has no material to think *with*. Isn't that true?"

"Yes—I know it; but how vexatious it is. Just because I can't know, I all the more *want* to know."

We sat silent a while turning the puzzle over in our minds: then all at once I saw how to find out, and was surprised that we had not thought of it in the beginning, it was so simple. I sprang up and said, "How stupid we are! Let us eat of it; we shall die, and then we shall know what it is, and not have any more bother about it."

Adam saw that it was the right idea, and he rose at once and was reaching for an apple when a most curious creature came floundering by, of a kind which we had never seen before, and of course we dropped a matter which was of no special scientific interest, to rush after one that was.

Miles and miles over hill and dale we chased that lumbering, scrambling, fluttering goblin till we were away down the western side of the valley where the pillared great banyan tree is, and there we caught him. What a joy, what a triumph: he is a pterodactyl! Oh, he is a love, he is so ugly! And has such a temper, and such an odious cry. We called a couple of tigers and rode home, and fetched him along, and now I have him by me, and it is late, but I can't bear to go to bed, he is such a fascinating fiend and such a royal contribution to science. I know I shan't sleep for thinking of him and longing for morning to come, so that I can explore him and scrutinize him, and search out the secret of his birth, and determine how much of him is bird and how much is reptile, and see if he is a survival of the fittest; which we think is doubtful, by the look of him.

Oh, Science, where thou art, all other interests fade and vanish away!

Adam wakes up. Asks me not to forget to set down those four new words. It shows that he has forgotten them. But I have not. For his sake I am always watching. They are down. It is he that is building the Dictionary—as he thinks—but I have noticed that it is I who do the work. But it is no matter, I like to do anything that he wants me to do; and in the case of the Dictionary I take special pleasure in the labor, because it saves him a humiliation, poor boy. His spelling is unscientific. He spells cat with a k, and catastrophe with a c, although both are from the same root.

Three days later. We have named him Terry, for short, and oh, he is a love! All these three days we have been wholly absorbed in him. Adam wonders how science ever got along without him till now, and I feel the same. The cat took a chance in him, seeing that he was a stranger, but has regretted it. Terry fetched Thomas a rake fore and aft which left much to be desired in the way of fur, and Thomas retired with the air of a person who had been intending to confer a surprise, and was now of a mind to go and think it over and see how it happened to go the other way. Terry is just grand—there's no other creature like him. Adam has examined him thoroughly, and feels sure he is a survival of the fittest. I think Thomas thinks otherwise.

Year 3. Early in July, Adam noticed that a fish in the pond was developing legs—a fish of the whale family, though not a true whale itself, it being in a state of arrested development. It was a tadpole. We watched it with great interest, for if the legs did really mature and become usable, it was our purpose to develop them in other fishes, so that they could come out and walk around and have more liberty. We had often been troubled about those poor creatures, always wet and uncomfortable, and always restricted to the water whilst the others were free to play amongst the flowers and have a pleasant time. Soon the legs were perfected, sure enough, and then the whale was a frog. It came ashore and hopped about and sang joyously, particularly in the evenings, and its gratitude was without bounds. Others followed rapidly, and soon we had abundant music, nights, which was a great improvement on the stillness which had prevailed before.

We brought various kinds of fishes ashore and turned them

loose in the meadows, but in all cases they were a disappointment—no legs came. It was strange; we could not understand it. Within a week they had all wandered back to the water, and seemed better satisfied there than they had been on land. We took this as evidence that fishes as a rule do not care for the land, and that none of them took any strong interest in it but the whales. There were some large whales in a considerable lake three hundred miles up the valley, and Adam went up there with the idea of developing them and increasing their enjoyment.

When he had been gone a week, little Cain was born. It was a great surprise to me, I was not aware that anything was going to happen. But it was just as Adam is always saying: "It is the unexpected that happens."

I did not know what to make of it at first. I took it for an animal. But it hardly seemed to be that, upon examination, for it had no teeth and hardly any fur, and was a singularly helpless mite. Some of its details were human, but there were not enough of them to justify me in scientifically classifying it under that head. Thus it started as a *lusus naturae*—a freak —and it was necessary to let it go at that, for the time being, and wait for developments.

However, I soon began to take an interest in it, and this interest grew day by day; presently this interest took a warmer cast and became affection, then love, then idolatry, and all my soul went out to the creature and I was consumed with a passion of gratitude and happiness. Life was become a bliss, a rapture, an ecstasy, and I longed, day by day, hour by hour, minute by minute for Adam for return and share my almost unendurable joy with me.

Year 4-5. At last he came, but he did not think it was a child. He meant well, and was dear and lovely, but he was scientist first and man afterward—it was his nature—and he could accept of nothing until it was scientifically proven. The alarms I passed through, during the next twelvemonth, with that student's experiments, are quite beyond description. He exposed the child to every discomfort and inconvenience he could imagine, in order to determine what kind of bird or reptile or quadruped it was, and what it was for, and so I had to follow him about, day and night, in weariness and despair to appease its poor little sorrows and help it to bear them the best it could. He believed I had found it in the woods, and I was glad and grateful to let him think so, because the idea beguiled him to go away at times and hunt for another, and this gave the child and me blessed seasons of respite and peace. No one can ever know the relief I felt whenever he ceased from his distressful experiments and gathered his traps and bait together and started for the woods. As soon as he was out of sight I hugged my precious to my heart and smothered it with kisses, and cried for thankfulness. The poor little thing seemed to realize that something fortunate for us had happened, and it would kick and crow, and spread its gummy mouth and smile the happy smile of childhood all the way down to its brains— or whatever those things are that are down in there.

Year 10. Next came our little Abel. I think we were a year and a half or two years old when Cain was born, and about three or three and a half when Abel was added. By this time Adam was getting to understand. Gradually his experiments grew less and less troublesome, and finally, within a year after the birth of Gladys and Edwina—years 5 and 6—ceased altogether. He came to love the children fondly, after he had gotten them scientifically classified, and from that time till now the bliss of Eden is perfect.

We have nine children, now—half boys and half girls.

Cain and Abel are beginning to learn. Already Cain can add as well as I can, and multiply and subtract a little. Abel is not as quick as his brother, mentally, but he has persistence, and that seems to answer in the place of quickness. Abel learns about as much in three hours as Cain does, but Cain gets a couple of hours out of it for play. So, Abel is a long time on the road, but, as Adam says, he "arrives on schedule, just the same." Adam has concluded that persistence is one of the talents, and has classified it under that head in his dictionary. Spelling is a gift, too, I am sure of it. With all Cain's brightness he cannot learn to spell. Now that is like his father, who is the brightest of us all, yet whose orthography is just a calamity. I can spell, and so can Abel. These several facts prove nothing, for one cannot deduce a principle from so few examples, but they do at least indicate that the ability to learn to spell correctly is a gift; that it is born in a person, and is a sign of intellectual inferiority. By parity of reasoning, its absence is a sign of great mental power. Sometimes, when Adam has worked a good large word like Ratiocination through his mill and is standing over the wreck mopping away his sweat, I could worship him he seems so intellectually grand and awful and sublime. He can spell Phthysic in more different ways than there are.

Cain and Abel are dear little chaps, and they take very nice care of their little brothers and sisters. The four eldest of the flock go wandering everywhere, according to their desire, and often we see nothing of them for two or three days together. Once they lost Gladys, and came back without her. They could not remember just where or when it was that they missed her. It was far away, they said, but they did not know how far; it was a new region for them. It was rich in berries of the plant which we call the deadly nightshade—for what reason we do not know. It hasn't any meaning, but it utilizes one of the words which we long ago got of the Voice, and we like to employ new words whenever a chance offers, and so make them workable and handy. They are fond of those berries, and they long wandered about, eating them; by and by when they were ready to go somewhere else, they missed Gladys, and she did not answer to her name.

Next day she did not come. Nor the next day, nor the day after that. Then three more days, and still she did not come. It was very strange; nothing quite the match of this had ever happened before. Our curiosity began to be excited. Adam was of the opinion that if she had not come next day, or at furthest the day after, we ought to send Cain and Abel to look.

So we did that. They were gone three days, but they found her. She had had adventures. In the dark, the first night, she fell in the river and was washed down a long distance, she did not know how far, and was finally flung upon a sandbar. After that, she lived with a kangaroo's family, and was hospitably entertained, and there was much sociability. The mama-kangaroo was very sweet and motherly, and would take her babies out of her pocket and go foraging among the hills and dales and fetch home a pocketful of the choicest fruits and nuts; and nearly every night there was company—bears and rabbits and buzzards and chickens and foxes and hyenas and polecats and other creatures—and gay romping and grand times. The animals seemed to pity the child because she had no fur; for always when she slept they covered her with leaves and moss to protect her dainty flesh, and she was covered like that when the boys found her. She had been homesick the first days, but had gotten over it.

That was her word—homesick. We have put it in the Dictionary, and will presently settle upon a meaning for it. It is

made of two words which we already had, and which have
clear meanings when by themselves, though apparently none
when combined. Building a dictionary is exceedingly interesting work, but tough; as Adam says. . . .

IV PASSAGE FROM EVE'S AUTOBIOGRAPHY YEAR OF THE WORLD, 920

*With the next passage we reach the ominous year that had come
almost to obsess the translator. We plunge into a modern world
whose complexity is highlighted by the simplicities described in the
earlier papers, and we begin with one of its most urgent problems,
overpopulation. It is at once clear that the second decade of the tenth
century After Creation seemed to the Father of History very much
like the first decade of the twentieth century After Christ. This
passage from Eve's autobiography (erroneously attributed to her
diary in the translator's notes) serves, with its quotation from a review, as a prelude to the more detailed study in the next chapter.*

   The date of this translation is, I think, 1906.

                                                    B. DV.

Ah, well, in that old simple, ignorant time it never entered
our unthinking heads that we, humble, unknown and incon-
sequential little people, were cradling, nursing and watching
over the most conspicuous and stupendous event which would
happen in the universe for a thousand years—the founding
of the human race!

   It is true that the world was a solitude in the first days, but
the solitude was soon modified. When we were 30 years old
we had 30 children, and our children had 300; in 20 years
more the population was 6,000; by the end of the second
century it was become millions. For we are a long-lived race,
and not many died. More than half of my children are still
alive. I did not cease to bear until I was approaching middle
age. As a rule, such of my children as survived the perils of
childhood have continued to live, and this has been the case
with the other families. Our race now numbers billions.

**EXTRACT FROM AN ARTICLE IN "THE RADICAL,"
JANUARY, 916**

. . . When the population reached five billions the earth was
heavily burdened to support it. But wars, pestilences and

famines brought relief, from time to time, and in some degree reduced the prodigious pressure. The memorable benefaction of the year 508, which was a famine reinforced by a pestilence, swept away sixteen hundred millions of people in nine months.

It was not much, but it was something. The same is all that can be said of its successors of later periods. The burden of population grew heavier and heavier and more and more formidable, century by century, and the gravity of the situation created by it was steadily and proportionately increased.

After the age of infancy, few died. The average of life was six hundred years. The cradles were filling, filling, filling—always, always, always; the cemeteries stood comparatively idle, the undertakers had but little traffic, they could hardly support their families. The death rate was 2,250 in the million. To the thoughtful this was portentous; to the light-witted it was matter for brag! These latter were always comparing the population of one decade with that of the previous one and hurrahing over the mighty increase—as if that were an advantage to the world; a world that could hardly scratch enough out of the earth to keep itself from starving.

And yet, worse was to come! Necessarily our true hope did not and could not lie in spasmodic famine and pestilence, whose effects could be only temporary, but in war and the physicians, whose help is constant. Now then, let us note what has been happening. In the past fifty years science has reduced the doctor's effectiveness by half. He uses but one deadly drug now, where formerly he used ten. Improved sanitation has made whole regions healthy which were previously not so. It has been discovered that the majority of the most useful and fatal diseases are caused by microbes of various breeds; very well, they have learned how to render the efforts of those microbes innocuous. As a result, yellow fever, black plague, cholera, diphtheria, and nearly every valuable distemper we had are become but entertainments for the idle hour, and are of no more value to the State than is the stomach-ache. Marvelous advances in surgery have been added to our disasters. They remove a diseased stomach, now, and the man gets along better and cheaper than he did before. If a man loses a faculty, they bore into his skull and restore it. They take off his legs and arms, and refurnish him from the mechanical junk shop, and he is as good as new. They give him a new nose if he needs it; new entrails; new bones; new teeth; glass eyes; silver tubes to swallow through; in a word, they take him to pieces and make him over again, and he can stand twice as much wear and tear as he could before. They do these things by help of antiseptics and anesthesia, and there is no gangrene and no pain. Thus war has become nearly valueless; out of a hundred wounded that would formerly have died, ninety-nine are back in the ranks again in a month.

What, then, is the grand result of all this microbing and sanitation and surgery? This—which is appalling: the death rate has been reduced to 1,200 in the million. And foolish people rejoice at it and boast about it! It is a serious matter. It promises to double the globe's population every twelve months. In time there will not be room in the world for the people to stand, let alone sit down.

Remedy? I know of none. The span of life is too long, the death rate is too trifling. The span should be thirty-five years— a mere moment of Time—the death rate should be 20,000 or 30,000 in the million. Even then the population would double in thirty-five years, and by and by even this would be a burden again and make the support of life difficult.

Honor to whom honor is due: the physician failed us, war has saved us. Not that the killed and wounded amount to anything as a relief, for they do not; but the poverty and desolation caused by war sweep myriads away and make space for immigrants. War is a rude friend, but a kind one. It keeps us down to sixty billion and saves the hard-grubbing world alive. It is all that the globe can support. . . .

V THE WORLD IN THE YEAR 920 AFTER CREATION

This section requires no annotation. The Family's world is ripe for destruction—and Noah is hammering at the Ark. We are surrounded by unmistakable evidence of social rot, adequately analyzed by the Mad Prophet and by the Professor of the Science of Historical Forecast who reports him. They are as familiar to us today as they were to the Father of History and I need only note that the hint here given of the Prodigy, the shoemaker-dictator, was apparently elaborated at length in other portions of the Adam papers which Mark Twain intended to translate but did not. There is a slight discrepancy in the texts; clearly, the Shoemaker appeared following the collapse of the democratic experiment which Methuselah's diary mentions and which occurred in the fifth century. But he was also a product of the industrial revolution, which is here attributed to the eighth

century. *The error must be subjective: Mark Twain was thinking of
the progress of science and invention in the nineteenth century after
Christ and believed that the next collapse of civilization was at hand
in the early twentieth century.*

*Corruptions and confusion of the texts in this part of the archives
caused the translator much trouble—which his editor was to repeat
after him. I have had to piece these translations together from a variety of manuscripts, fragmentary, half-deleted, partly revised, with few
clues to the order that Mark Twain intended them to have. I have
arranged them in what seems to me a proper sequence, in a sequence
which at least progressively describes the chaos of society. I cannot
date any of the manuscripts but I think that they were all written in
1906. Possibly the "Lecture" may be earlier than that; in fact, it may
be earlier than any other of the papers except Methuselah's diary.*

B. DV.

FROM THE DIARY OF A LADY OF THE BLOOD, THIRD GRADE

Received the Mad Prophet today. He is a good man, and I
think his intellect is better than its reputation. He got his nickname long ago, and did not deserve it; for he merely builds
prognostications, not prophecies. He pretends to nothing
more. Builds them out of history and statistics, using the facts
of the past to forecast the probabilities of the future. It is
merely applied science. An astronomer foretells an eclipse, yet
is not obnoxious to the charge of pretending to be a prophet.
Noah is a prophet; and certainly no one has more reverence
for him and for his sacred office than has this modest dealer
in probabilities and prognostications.

I have known the Mad Prophet—or the Mad Philosopher,
for he has both names—ever since he was a student in college,
in the beginning of the third century. He was nineteen or
twenty then. I have always had a kindly feeling for him; partly,
of course, because he was a relative (though distant), but
mainly, I am sure, because of the good qualities of his head
and heart. He married when he was twenty-four, and when
neither he nor the girl was properly situated to marry, for they
were poor and belonged to families which had the same defect.
Both families were respectable enough, and in a faraway
fashion were allied to the nobility; but as Adam always said,
"Respectability butters no parsnips," and it was not just the
right capital to marry on. I advised them to wait a while, and
of course they did it, since advice from a Personage of the

Blood was—and is—law, by courtesy and custom of the race; but they were an impatient little pair and dreadfully in love with each other, and they only waited long enough to cover the bare necessities of etiquette. My influence got the lad a small mathematics professorship in his university and kept him in possession of it, and he worked hard and saved faithfully. Poor things, they endured the suspension of life, as they called it, as long as they could; they waited sixty years, then they got married. She was a lovely little rat, and sweetly captivating: slender, lissome, brown-eyed, dimpled, complexioned like a peach blossom, frisky, frolicsome, graceful—just a picture, she was, just a poem. She was of foreign extraction; her little drop of nobility had trickled down to her, in the lapse of time, from a great lord whose habitat was in a remote land many meridians of longitude away, the Duke of Washoe. He was descended from me through—I forget the name, now —but the source was my daughter Regina's branch, I mean the one proceeding from Regina's second marriage. He was second cousin to—but I have forgotten that name, too. The little bride's name was Red Cloud, and was as foreign as her extraction. It was a kind of inheritance.

The couple remained poor, and are poor yet, but as happy as many that are richer. They have always had enough for their needs, for my influence has kept him in his post, and has also augmented his salary a little, more than once. Their tranquil life has suffered one blight, one heavy sorrow, which fell upon them toward the end of the first century of their union, and whose shadow lies upon their hearts yet. They lost sixteen children in a railway accident.

Before he came, today, the Philosopher had been examining the mobile which is propelled by the wonderful new force, liquefied thought. He was profoundly impressed. He said he could see no reason why this force should not displace steam and electricity, since it is much more powerful than those agents, occupies almost no space, and costs next to nothing. That is, the cost to the Trust that owns the patent is next to nothing. It is the same Trust that owns the globe's railways and ships—the globe's transportation, in a word.

"Five years ago," said he, "this new force was laughed at by the ignorant, and discounted by the wise—a thing which always happens when there is a new invention. It happened with the Liograph, it happened with the Hellograph, it happened with the Mumble'n'screechograph, and it will go on happening with new inventions to the end of time. Why cannot people learn to wait for developments before they commit themselves? Surely experience has given them warnings enough. Almost as a rule the apparently insane invention turns out well by and by, through the discovery and application to it of improvements of one kind and another. Five years ago liquefied thought had no value but as an Imperial Academy Show on Ladies' Night. The cost of production was prohibitory, as far as business and commerce were concerned, for at that stage of development the only raw material which would answer had to be taken from statesmen, judges, scientists, poets, philosophers, editors, sculptors, painters, generals, admirals, inventors, engineers, and such like, but now—as Methuselah says—you can get it from politicians and idiots; adding, in his unpleasant way, 'But that is tautology; politician and idiot are synonymous terms.'

"I am of the opinion that the development of this mysterious new force has not yet proceeded beyond the infancy stage. I think we know but little about it now, compared with what we shall know a few decades hence. Why, it may turn out to be the renowned and lamented Lost Force of old tradition! And it isn't mere tradition; there is history for it. You know the tradition yourself, gracious Excellency,—like the rest of the world—but you do not know the history. It has just been deciphered from the clay archives of an exhumed city of the Double Continent; and when it is published the nations will perceive that when the amazing man called 'the Prodigy,' who rose out of obscurity in the middle of the fifth century and in a few years conquered the world and brought all its kingdoms under his imperial scepter, where they still abide under the scepter of his son today, had formidable help in his stupendous work from a source outside of his colossal genius for war, statesmanship, and administration, unrivaled and unapproachable as these confessedly were. That source was the agent known to tradition, romance, and poetry as the Lost Force. It is true that that humble young shoemaker did sweep the Double Continent from end to end with fire and sword without that help, to establish his autocratic sway over all its monarchies by merely the faculties that were born in him, and that he handled a billion men in the field under a million generals trained by himself and subject to his sole will unhampered by meddling ministries and legislatures, and left mountains of dead and wounded upon his battlefields, but he

subdued the rest of the globe without spilling blood, except
in a single instance.

"That mystery is explained, now, by the clay records. It
came to his knowledge that one Napeer, an obscure person
but learned in science, had stated in his will that he had discovered a means whereby he could sweep a whole army out
of existence in an instant, but that he would not reveal his
secret, since war was already terrible enough and he would not
be a party to the augmentation of its destructiveness.

"The shoemaker-emperor said, 'The man was foolish—his
invention would abolish war altogether,' and commanded that
all papers left behind by him should be brought to him. He
found the formula, mastered its details, then destroyed it. He
privately manufactured that tremendous agent, and went out
alone against the sovereigns of the eastern world, with it in his
pocket. Only one army ever came against him. It formed itself
in battle array in a great plain, and at a distance of twelve
miles he blew it into the air, leaving no vestige of it behind but
a few rags and buttons.

"He claimed the sovereignty of the globe and it was accorded him without an objecting voice. As you are aware, his
reign of thirty years was a reign of peace; then, by accident, he
blew himself up with his machine, along with one of his vice-
regal capitals, and his formidable secret died with him. Then
the dreadful wars began again, and for the world's sins they
still continue. But the universal empire which he established
was founded in wisdom and strength, and today his son sits as
securely upon its throne as he did when he mounted it so
many centuries ago."

It was quite interesting. He was just beginning to speak
about his "Law of Periodical Repetition"—or perhaps it was
about his "Law of the Permanency of the Intellectual Average"
—but was interrupted. He was to be received by her Grandeur,
and was now called to that exalted privilege by an officer of the
Household.

EXTRACT FROM THE DISCOURSE OF REGINALD SELKIRK,
THE MAD PHILOSOPHER, TO HER GRANDEUR, THE ACTING
HEAD OF THE HUMAN RACE

"Our wonderful civilization? I will not object to the adjective
—it rightly describes it—but I do object to the large and com-

placent admiration which it implies. By all accounts—yours in chief, Excellency—the pure and sweet and ignorant and un-sordid civilization of Eden was worth a thousand millions of it. What is a civilization, rightly considered? Morally, it is the evil passions repressed, the level of conduct raised; spiritually, idols cast down, God enthroned; materially, bread and fair treatment for the greatest number. That is the common for-mula, the common definition; everybody accepts it and is satisfied with it.

"Our civilization is wonderful, in certain spectacular and meretricious ways; wonderful in scientific marvels and inven-tive miracles; wonderful in material inflation, which it calls advancement, progress, and other pet names; wonderful in its spying-out of the deep secrets of Nature and its vanquishment of her stubborn laws; wonderful in its extraordinary financial and commercial achievements; wonderful in its hunger for money, and in its indifference as to how it is acquired; won-derful in the hitherto undreamed-of magnitude of its private fortunes and the prodigal fashion in which they are given away to institutions devoted to the public culture; wonderful in its exhibitions of poverty; wonderful in the surprises which it gets out of that great new birth, Organization, the latest and most potent creation and miracle-worker of the commercialized in-tellect, as applied in transportation systems, in manufactures, in systems of communication, in news-gathering, book-publish-ing, journalism; in protecting labor; in oppressing labor; in herding the national parties and keeping the sheep docile and usable; in closing the public service against brains and char-acter; in electing purchasable legislatures, blatherskite Con-gresses, and city governments which rob the town and sell municipal protection to gamblers, thieves, prostitutes, and professional seducers for cash. It is a civilization which has destroyed the simplicity and repose of life; replaced its con-tentment, its poetry, its soft romance-dreams and visions with the money-fever, sordid ideals, vulgar ambitions, and the sleep which does not refresh; it has invented a thousand useless luxuries, and turned them into necessities; it has created a thousand vicious appetites and satisfies none of them; it has dethroned God and set up a shekel in His place.

"Religion has removed from the heart to the mouth. You have the word of Noah for it. Time was, when two sects, divided but by a single hair of doctrine, would fight for that hair, would kill, torture, persecute for it, die for it. That religion was in the heart; it was vital, it was a living thing, it was the very man himself. Who fights for his religion now, but with the mouth? Your civilization has brought the flood. Noah has said it, and he is preparing."

PASSAGE FROM A LECTURE

The monthly meeting of the Imperial Institute took place on the 18th. With but two exceptions the seats of the Forty Immortals were occupied. The lecturer of the evening was the distinguished Professor of the Science of Historical Forecast. A part of his subject concerned two of the Laws of Reginald Selkirk, commonly called the Mad Philosopher, namely, the "Law of Intellectual Averages" and the "Law of Periodical Repetition." After a consideration, at some length, of cognate matters, he said:

"I regard these Laws as established. By the terms of the Law of Periodical Repetition nothing whatever can happen a single time only; everything happens again, and yet again, and still again—monotonously. Nature has no originality—I mean, no large ability in the matter of inventing new things, new ideas, new stage effects. She has a superb and amazing and infinitely varied equipment of old ones, but she never adds to them. She repeats—repeats—repeats—repeats. Examine your memory and your experience; you will find it is true. When she puts together a man, and is satisfied with him, she is loyal to him, she stands by him through thick and thin forevermore, she repeats him by billions and billions of examples; and physically and mentally the average remains exactly the same, it doesn't vary a hair between the first batch, the middle batch and the last batch. If you ask, 'But really—do you think all men are alike?' I reply, ' I said the average does not vary.'

" 'But you will have to admit that some individuals do far overtop the average—intellectually, at least.'

"Yes, I answer, and Nature repeats *those*. There is nothing that she doesn't repeat. If I may use a figure, she has established the general intellectual level of the race at say, six feet. Take any billion men and stand them in a mass, and their headtops will make a floor—a floor as level as a table. That floor represents the intellectual altitude of the masses —and it never changes. Here and there, miles apart, a head

will project above it a matter of one intellectual inch, so
to speak—men of mark in science, law, war, commerce, etc.;
in a spread of five thousand miles you will find three heads
that project still an inch higher, men of national fame—and
one that is higher than those by two inches, maybe three—
a man of (temporarily) world-wide renown; and finally, somewhere around the circumference of the globe, you will find,
once in five centuries of waiting, one majestic head which
overtops the highest of all the others—an author, a teacher,
an artist, a martyr, a conqueror, whose fame towers to the
stars, and whose fame will never perish, never fade, while
time shall last; some colossus supreme above all the human
herd, some unmated and unmatable prodigy like him who,
by magic of the forces born in him, turned his shoe-hammer
into the scepter of universal dominion. Now in that view you
have the ordinary man of all nations; you have the here-and-
there man that is larger-brained and becomes distinguished;
you have the still rarer man of still wider and more lasting
distinction; and in that final head rising solitary out of the
stretch of the ages, you have the limit of Nature's output.

"Will she change this program? Not while time lasts. Will
she repeat it forever? Yes. Forever and ever she will do those
grades over and over again, always in the same proportions,
and always with the regularity of a machine. In each million
of people, just so many inch-superiorities; in each billion, just
so many two-inch superiorities—and so on; and always that
recurrent solitary star once in an age, never oftener, never
two of them at a time.

"Nature, when pleased with an idea, never tires of applying
it. She makes plains; she makes hills; she makes mountains;
raises a conspicuous peak at wide intervals; then loftier and
rarer ones, continents apart; and finally a supreme one six
miles high. She uses this grading process in horses; she turns
out myriads of them that are all of one common dull gait;
with here and there a faster one; at enormous intervals a conspicuously faster one; and once in a half-century a celebrity
that does a mile in two minutes. She will repeat that horse
every fifty years to the end of time.

"By the Law of Periodical Repetition, everything which has
happened once must happen again and again and again—
and not capriciously, but at regular periods, and each thing
in its own period, not another's and each obeying its own
law. The eclipse of the sun, the occultation of Venus, the

arrival and departure of the comets, the annual shower of stars—all these things hint to us that the same Nature which delights in periodical repetition in the skies is the Nature which orders the affairs of the earth. Let us not underrate the value of that hint.

"Are there any ingenuities whereby you can discredit the law of suicide? No. It is established. If there was such and such a number in such and such a town last year, that number, substantially will be repeated this year. That number will keep step, arbitrarily, with the increase of population, year after year. Given the population a century hence, you can determine the crop of suicides that will be harvested in that distant year.

"Will this wonderful civilization of today perish? Yes, everything perishes. Will it rise and exist again? It will—for nothing can happen that will not happen again. And again, and still again, forever. It took more than eight centuries to prepare this civilization—then it suddenly began to grow, and in less than a century it is become a bewildering marvel. In time, it will pass away and be forgotten. Ages will elapse, then it will come again; and not incomplete, but complete; not an invention nor discovery nor any smallest detail of it missing. Again it will pass away, and after ages will rise and dazzle the world again as it dazzles it now —perfect in all its parts once more. It is the Law of Periodical Repetition.

"It is even possible that the mere names of things will be reproduced. Did not the Science of Health rise, in the old time, and did it not pass into oblivion, and has it not latterly come again and brought with it its forgotten name? Will it perish once more? Many times, I think, as the ages drift on; and still come again and again. And the forgotten book, *Science and Health, with Key to the Scriptures*—is it not with us once more, revised, corrected, and its orgies of style and construction tamed by an educated disciple? Will it not yet die, once, twice, a dozen times, and still at vast intervals rise again and successfully challenge the mind of man to understand it? We may not doubt it. By the Law of Periodical Repetitions it must happen."

PASSAGE FROM THE DIARY OF THE MAD PHILOSOPHER

Received in audience by the Most Illustrious, Most Powerful, Most Gracious, Most Reverend, her Grandeur, the Acting

Head of the Human Race, whom I addressed by these her
official titles, and humbly thanked her, kneeling; then by
permission indicated by a gesture, rose and stood before the
Throne. It was in the Hall of Sovereigns, in the same palace
which she and the Family have occupied I do not know
how many centuries, and which they prefer to any other. It
is still the most gorgeous—and I think the most beautiful,
too—in the Empire. Its gilded masses cover miles of space,
and blaze like a fallen sun. Its interior parks and gardens and
forests stretch away into the mellow distances, an apparently
limitless paradise. A hundred thousand persons, not counting
the brigades and divisions of Household Troops, serve the
Parents and certain Eden-born families of their immediate
descendants in this place. Yet the palace takes up no inordi-
nate room in this monster capital, whose population almost
defies figures, and which contains many streets that are upwards of two hundred miles long without a break.

The Hall of Sovereigns is a glittering vast rotunda which
ancient masters of all the arts wrought into a vision of glory
and beauty with sculptured marbles and incrusted gems and
costly goldwork and sunset splendors of color, and there the
monarchs of all the globe have assembled every fifty years,
with their officers of state, to do homage to the Parents of
the Race. Spaciousness is requisite, and there is no lack of
it. It must be a fine sight to see that multitude of black kings
and white, yellow kings and brown, all in their dazzle of rich
outlandish costumes; and it must be a bank holiday for in-
terpreters, too. But the place was only sparsely peopled, now
—guards, chamberlains, pages, and their sort, with a proper
showing of secretaries ready and prepared to do nothing, and
doing it.

Her Grandeur was clothed as the Arctic skies are clothed
when the northern lights flood them with their trembling
waves of purple and crimson and golden flame, and through
this shifting and changing dream of rich colors the flash of
innumerable jewels went chasing and turning, gleaming and
expiring like trains of sparks through burnt paper. Afterward
I spoke with enthusiasm of this brilliant spectacle to Nanga
Parbat, that soured and dissolute Eden-born Scion of the First
Blood whose bad heart banishment from the Presence long
ago filled with malice and hate and envy, and he smiled a
vinegar smile and said with scorn, "Pah! these airs! I've seen
the day when the Family hadn't a shirt amongst them."

I could not resent this; one of my degree is not permitted to talk back to an Eden-born, even if one were so disposed, which is a thought which could exist only a passionate moment or two in a loyal breast; but I begged him to spare me such words about the Powers That Be, it being improper that I should hear them.

"Oh, of course!" he scoffed. "You are a Patriot—you and your sort. And what is a Patriot, pray? It's one who grovels to the Family, and shouts for the Emperor and the Government, be they in the right or in the wrong,—and especially when they are in the wrong; that they call 'standing by the Country.' Patriotism—oh, Laura! that sham, that perversion, that silver-gilt nursery-bauble wherewith this combination of Land-grabbers, Constitution-tinkers, imbeciles and hypocrites called the Imperial Government beguiles and captures those confiding children the People. Oh, it's a sweet thing, is Patriotism. Adam used to call it 'the last refuge of a scoundrel.' Do you know, I've been called a Patriot myself, by the ignorant and the thoughtless. Alas and alas, in this world one is never safe from insult. Come and take something?"

It was an odiously embarrassing position, people passing and staring all the time, wondering to see a Scion of the First Blood and wearing the sacred uniform of his Order (noticeably the worse for wear, by the way) familiarly buttonholing one of my estate, just as if I were an equal. And he could hardly fail to be overheard, for he would talk in a frank free voice (being "under the influence," as the saying is), do what I might to quiet him. In order to get away from observation I went into the Eden Arms with him, and of course found respite and peace, the customers respectfully vacating the place and filing out uncovered.

"Slaves!" he snarled; "look at them! They abase themselves before clothes and the accident of birth—silver-gilt nursery-baubles again—Lord, it sizes up the quality of the human race!" and he rasped out a sardonic chuckle. "The human race, that has such a fine opinion of itself." He inspected his sacred uniform, detached a hanging rag of gold lace from it, musingly turned it this way and that in his fingers, then threw it to a dog, who sniffed at it hopefully a moment, then left it lying and slouched away disappointed. "Now there's a rational creature, a respect-worthy creature—I do him homage!" He passed his fingers through his thatch of snow, and said with a sigh, "Ah, well, we were once as wise as he, and as sane—I have seen that day."

Soon he broke into a tirade again—this time about nepotism. He did not go quite so far as to mention names, but it was plain enough that his target was the Acting Head of the Race, his grandmother. It made the flesh crawl to hear him.

"There isn't a place of value in that palace," he said, "that goes by merit; not a rich sinecure but is encumbered by some incapable dotard whose only qualification is that he belongs by accident of birth in one or another of the First Three Grades of the Blood. Everything worth having is saved for the Three Orders—and how they do hang on, those jibbering senilities! Adam used to sigh and say, 'They seldom die, and never resign.' Nepotism? it's just a buzzard's nest of it. She —why, dear me, she can't endure the touch or smell of plebeian flesh, the very scullery maids must be of the Family— Third Grade, Herald's Office certificate, no Bar Sinister in the line, 'No Irish need apply,' as the slang saying is. Oh, the sarcasm of it—why, she was never married, herself!"

I ventured to rebuke him, saying, "She was born married."

"Huh!" he scoffed, and snapped his fingers; "tell it to the marines."

Then he went on and on about nepotism, and there was nothing too bitter for him to say. I could have reminded him, if it had been meet for one of my condition to say such a thing, that if the system was evil none had gotten more advantage out of it than himself; for, through no merit but his Blood alone, he had served in the palace a couple of centuries, in a descending scale of offices sacred to the Third Degree, discrediting and degrading each in turn until he got down to boot-polisher; and not until it was found that he was even able to bring dishonor upon that was he at last given up in despair and forbidden the premises.

He attacked in turn everything that one respects and reveres, and I was obliged to stay and listen, for he is a capricious in his humors and might have taken mortal offense if I had asked for my dismissal. But finally, without preliminary or circumlocution he suddenly said he was tired of my monotonous gabble, and waved his hand toward the door. It was unjust, for it was he that had done the talking, I had said hardly a word; but I backed immediately out of the Presence without protest, being glad to go on any terms. Almost immediately he himself emerged and marched down the street, the people falling apart before him and bowing and scraping as he passed, he taking no notice of them. As disagreeable a scamp as I know—of that I am certain.

In spirit, in speech and in looks he was a sorrowful contrast to his noble grandam. Long ago she was rebellious, it is said, and would not be appeased; but trouble and the burden of the ages have chastened her heart and restored to it the charity and gentleness that were its birthright, and their grace is in her face, which is beautiful. It was a privilege to see her again. I had not seen her since the first year of the new century, when she drove in state and showed herself to the people, in the glare of the illuminations, and formally inaugurated the Epoch, in accordance with antique custom—always an impressive function, but peculiarly and movingly so on this occasion, it being the first time she had ever performed it alone.

No eye fell unmoistened upon the vacant place at her side, a place not likely ever to be occupied again. Eighty years ago, owing to failing health, his Serene Supremacy the Head of the Race resigned his functions into the hands of his Consort—though not his Authority—and since then has taken no active part in the administration of the Family's affairs, except that fifty-five years ago he received the Emperor of the World in private audience upon an occasion of urgency, and was persuaded to do the like again thirty-one years later. He has lived continuously in retirement in the hands of his physicians during the past three-quarters of a century, and by help of the advancing efficiency of medical science year by year for the past half-century has been mercifully enabled to retain his frail hold upon life. It is truly wonderful what the physicians have done; it is hardly too much to call it miraculous. It has made immense fame for them throughout the world, and prosperity as well.

PASSAGE FROM DIARY OF ———————*
  * Not filled out. Possibly Nanga Parbat's diary? [B. DV.]

. . . His exact condition has been at no time revealed to the public—certainly not by the physicians' bulletins. The sophisticated among us know how to discount those, it being quite understood that it is reputation in a physician's pocket to multiply an illustrious patient's danger by sixteen or twenty from time to time and then acquire the world's astonished admiration and reverence—and business—by pulling him up again to where he can take spoon victuals, and smile a sappy smile, and do some taffy about "my beloved peoples" to be cabled around the earth and sniveled about in the papers and utilized by the pulpit to mellow up the congregations and enable it to take another go at the contribution-pump. In all these decades he has never had anything really the matter with him but doctor-sickness—the understudy of one of the professional nurses told me so. Such of us as are not asses know what that disease is for, and who creates it, and how it is worked, and the money that is in it, and the reputation. Strictly select, strictly aristocratic, confined to the rich and renowned, is doctor-sickness; and for steady lastingness can give points to immortality.

To my certain knowledge, privately acquired from the understudy, the doctors have worked the stock market on this case from the start, selling bulletins to the brokers a week in advance—sometimes to such as were long on danger, sometimes to such as were short. Once, with consols at 102, they secretly treated with both parties, offering to send the market up to 108 in the one case or down to 94 in the other, according to the best bid. It is a fact; the understudy told me so. The bulls got it; she told me that, too. In innumerable other cases they have sold for a rise or a fall, though she did not know the figures. One can see by this what value a bulletin is, where the patient has doctor-sickness. Well, it's a [word illegible] of a world!

VI TWO FRAGMENTS FROM A SUPPRESSED BOOK CALLED "GLANCES AT HISTORY" OR "OUTLINES OF HISTORY"

These two fragments belong here but can be no further identified. The suppressed book is mentioned nowhere else, and if the Adam papers contained any more of it, at least Mark Twain translated no more. The two passages treat of a correspondence between the collapse of democracy in Methuselah's middle years and the one which, in 1906, the Father of History believed to be imminent. He was thinking of the occupation of the Philippines and, in the second fragment, of Theodore Roosevelt's Executive Order No. 78, both of which had analogies in the Adamic plutocracy.

Nothing has been omitted. The marks of elision at the beginning of each passage are Mark Twain's own.

                           B. DV.

. . . In a speech which he made more than five hundred years ago, and which has come down to us intact, he said:

We, free citizens of the Great Republic, feel an honest pride in her greatness, her strength, her just and gentle government, her wide liberties, her honored name, her stainless history, her unsmirched flag, her hands clean from oppression of the weak and from malicious conquest, her hospitable door that stands open to the hunted and the persecuted of all nations; we are proud of the judicious respect in which she is held by the monarchies which hem her in on every side, and proudest of all of that lofty patriotism which we inherited from our fathers, which we have kept pure, and which won our liberties in the beginning and has preserved them unto this day. While that patriotism endures the Republic is safe, her greatness is secure, and against them the powers of the earth cannot prevail.

I pray you to pause and consider. Against our traditions we are now entering upon an unjust and trivial war, a war against a helpless people, and for a base object—robbery. At first our citizens spoke out against this thing, by an impulse natural to their training. Today they have turned, and their voice is the other way. What caused the change? Merely a politician's trick—a high-sounding phrase, a blood-stirring phrase which turned their uncritical heads: Our Country, right or wrong! An empty phrase, a silly phrase. It was shouted by every newspaper, it was thundered from the pulpit, the Superintendent of Public Instruction placarded it in every schoolhouse in the land, the War Department inscribed it upon the flag. And every man who failed to shout it or who was silent, was proclaimed a traitor—none but those others were patriots. To be a patriot, one had to say, and keep on saying, "Our Country, right or wrong," and urge on the little war. Have you not perceived that that phrase is an insult to the nation?

For in a republic, who is "the Country"? Is it the Government which is for the moment in the saddle? Why, the Government is merely a servant—merely a temporary servant; it cannot be its prerogative to determine what is right and what is wrong, and decide who is a patriot and who isn't. Its function is to obey orders, not originate them. Who, then, is "the Country"? Is it the newspaper? is it the pulpit? is it the school superintendent? Why, these are mere parts of the country, not the whole of it; they have not command, they have only their little share in the command. They are but one in the thousand; it is in the thousand that command is lodged; they must determine what is right and what is wrong; they must decide who is a patriot and who isn't.

Who are the thousand—that is to say, who are "the Country"? In a monarchy, the king and his family are the country; in a republic it is the common voice of the people. Each of you, for himself, by himself and on his own responsibility, must speak. And it is a solemn and weighty responsibility, and not lightly to be flung aside at the bullying of pulpit, press, government, or the empty catch-phrases of politicians. Each must for himself alone decide what is right and what is wrong, and which course is patriotic and which isn't. You cannot shirk this and be a man. To decide it against your convictions is to be an unqualified and inexcusable traitor, both to yourself and to your country, let men label you as they may. If you alone of all the nation shall decide one way, and that way be the right way according to your convictions of the right, you have done your duty by yourself and by your country— hold up your head! You have nothing to be ashamed of.

Only when a republic's life is in danger should a man uphold his government when it is in the wrong. There is no other time.

This Republic's life is not in peril. The nation has sold its honor for a phrase. It has swung itself loose from its safe anchorage and is drifting, its helm is in pirate hands. The stupid phrase needed help, and it got another one: "Even if the war be wrong we are in it and must fight it out: *we cannot retire from it without dishonor.*" Why, not even a burglar could have said it better. We cannot withdraw from this sordid raid because to grant peace to those little people upon their terms —independence—would dishonor us. You have flung away Adam's phrase—you should take it up and examine it again. He said, *"An inglorious peace is better than a dishonorable war."*

You have planted a seed, and it will grow.

. . . But it was impossible to save the Great Republic. She was rotten to the heart. Lust of conquest had long ago done its work; trampling upon the helpless abroad had taught her, by a natural process, to endure with apathy the like at home; multitudes who had applauded the crushing of other people's liberties, lived to suffer for their mistake in their own persons.

The government was irrevocably in the hands of the prodigiously rich and their hangers-on; the suffrage was become a mere machine, which they used as they chose. There was no principle but commercialism, no patriotism but of the pocket. From showily and sumptuously entertaining neighboring titled aristocracies, and from trading their daughters to them, the plutocrats came in the course of time to hunger for titles and heredities themselves. The drift toward monarchy, in some form or other, began; it was spoken of in whispers at first, later in a bolder voice.

It was now that the portent called "the Prodigy" rose in the far south. Army after army, sovereignty after sovereignty went down under the mighty tread of the shoemaker, and still he held his conquering way—north, always north. The sleeping Republic awoke at last, but too late. It drove the money-changers from the temple, and put the government into clean hands—but all to no purpose. To keep the power in their own hands, the money-changers had long before bought up half the country with soldier-pensions and turned a measure which had originally been a righteous one into a machine for the manufacture of bondslaves—a machine which was at the same time an irremovable instrument of tyranny—for every pensioner had a vote, and every man and woman who had ever been acquainted with a soldier was a pensioner; pensions were dated back to the Fall, and hordes of men who had never handled a weapon in their lives came forward and drew three hundred years' back pay. The country's conquests, so far from being profitable to the treasury, had been an intolerable burden from the beginning. The pensions, the conquests, and corruption together had brought bankruptcy in spite of the maddest taxation; the government's credit was gone, the arsenals were empty, the country unprepared for war. The military and naval schools, and all commissioned offices in the army and navy, were the preserve of the money-changers; and the standing army—the creation of the conquest days—was their property.

The army and navy refused to serve the new Congress and the new Administration, and said ironically, "What are you going to do about it?" A difficult question to answer. Landsmen manned such ships as were not abroad watching the conquests—and sunk them all, in honest attempts [to] do their duty. A civilian army, officered by civilians, rose brimming with the patriotism of an old forgotten day and rushed multitudinously to the front, armed with sporting guns and pitchforks—and the standing army swept it into space. For the money-changers had privately sold out to the shoemaker. He conferred titles of nobility upon the money-changers, and mounted the Republic's throne without firing a shot.

It was thus that Popoatahualpacatapetl became our master; whose mastership descended in a little while to the Second of that name, who still holds it by his Viceroy this day.

VII EXTRACT FROM SHEM'S DIARY OF 920 A.C.

This was Mark Twain's last translation from the Adamic. It is at least as late as 1907 and possibly belongs to 1908. There is evidence that he meant to go on and translate more of what must have been a long and stirring record. Shem would probably have described the deluge, Ararat, and the bright new world. But Mark's interest finally flickered out—because he preferred to treat the Ark in "Letters from the Earth"?—and we end at an appropriate and symbolic moment, with Methuselah jeering at his deluded relatives, the populace deriding its prophet, and the world spinning on toward destruction.

B. DV.

Sabbath Day—As usual—nobody keeping it. Nobody but our family. Multitudes of the wicked swarming everywhere, and carousing. Drinking, fighting, dancing, gambling, laughing, shouting, singing—men, women, girls, youths, all at it. And at other infamies besides—infamies not to be set down in words. And the noise! Blowing of horns, banging on pots and kettles, blaring of brazen instruments, boom and clatter of drums—it is enough to burst a person's ears. And this is the Sabbath —think of it! Father says it was not like this in the earlier times. When he was a boy everybody kept the Day, and there was no wickedness, no pleasuring, no noise; there was peace, silence, tranquillity; there was divine service several times a day and in the evening. This was near six hundred years ago. Think of that time and this! One can hardly believe such a change could come in so little a while that men not yet old can remember it.

These horrible creatures have come in even greater crowds than usual, today, to look at the Ark, and prowl over it and

make fun of it. They ask questions, and when they are told
it is a boat, they laugh, and ask where the water is, out here
in the dry plain. When we say the Lord is going to send the
water from heaven and drown all the world, they mock again,
and say, "Tell it to the marines."

Methuselah was here again today. While he isn't the oldest
person in the world, he is the oldest distinguished person in it,
and because of that peculiar supremacy, he is regarded with
awe by everybody; and wherever he appears the riotings cease
and silence falls upon the multitude, and they uncover and
salute him with slavish reverence as he passes by, murmuring
to each other, "Look at him—there he goes— 'most a thousand years old—used to know Adam, they say." He is a vain
old creature, and anybody can see how it gratifies him, though
he dodders along with his nose in the air and a simpering cake-
walk gait, pretending to be pondering some great matter
profoundly, and letting on that he doesn't know anything is
happening.

I know, from certain things I have noticed, that he is of
a jealous disposition; envious, too. Perhaps I ought not to
say this, for I am related to him by marriage, my wife
being his great-great-great-great-great-great-great-great-great-
great-great-great-great-great-great-granddaughter, or somewhere
along there, and indeed I wouldn't say it in public, but I think
there can be no harm in my saying it in the privacy of my
diary, which is merely the same as saying it to myself. He is
jealous about this Ark, I am quite sure of it. Jealous because
he wasn't asked to build it instead of Father. The Ark is such
a wonder to all the nations around that it has raised Father
from obscurity to world-wide fame, and Methuselah is jealous
of that. At first, people used to say, "Noah?—pray who is
Noah?"—but now they come miles to get his autograph. It
makes Methuselah tired.

He doesn't have to sit up nights doing autographs, but we
do. All of us—the whole eight; for Father can't do them all,
nor even a tenth of them, his hand being old and stiff.
Methuselah has a most unpleasant disposition. I think he is
never happy except when he is making other people uncomfortable. He always speaks of my brothers and me and our
wives as "the children." He does it because he sees that it
hurts our feelings. One day Japheth timidly ventured to remind him that we were men and women. You could have
heard him scoff a mile! And he closed his eyes in a kind of

ecstasy of scorn, and puckered his withered lips, exposing his yellow fangs and the gaps between them, and hacked out a dry odious laugh with an asthmatic cough mixed with it, and said, "Men and women—the likes of you! Pray how old are you venerable relics?"

"Our wives are nearly eighty; and of us I am the youngest and I was a hundred last spring."

"Eighty, dear me! a hundred, dear me! And married! dear, dear, dear! You cradle-rubbish! You rag dolls! Married! In my young days nobody would ever have thought of such a thing as children getting married. It's monstrous!"

Japheth started to remind him that more than one of the patriarchs had married in early youth, but he wouldn't listen! That is just his way; if you catch him out with an argument that he can't answer, he raises his voice and shouts you down, and the only thing you can do is to shut your mouth and drop the matter. It won't do to dispute with him; it would be considered a scandal, and irreverent. At least it would not do for us boys to talk back. Neither us nor anybody else. Except the surgeon. The surgeon isn't afraid of him, and hasn't any reverence, anyway. The surgeon says a man is just a man, and his being a thousand years old doesn't make him any more than a man.

Letter to the Earth

OFFICE OF THE RECORDING ANGEL
Department of Petitions, Jan. 20

Abner Scofield
Coal Dealer
Buffalo, New York

I have the honor, as per command, to inform you that your recent act of benevolence and self-sacrifice has been recorded upon a page of the Book called *Golden Deeds of Men*; a distinction, I am permitted to remark, which is not merely extraordinary, it is unique.

As regards your prayers, for the week ending the 19th, I have the honor to report as follows:

1. For weather to advance hard coal 15 cents a ton. Granted.

2. For influx of laborers to reduce wages 10 percent. Granted.

3. For a break in rival soft-coal prices. Granted.

4. For a visitation upon the man, or upon the family of the man, who has set up a competing retail coal-yard in Rochester. Granted, as follows: diphtheria, 2, 1 fatal; scarlet fever, 1, to result in deafness and imbecility. NOTE. This prayer should have been directed against this subordinate's principals, the N. Y. Central R. R. Co.

5. For deportation to Sheol of annoying swarms of persons who apply daily for work, or for favors of one sort or another. Taken under advisement for later decision and compromise, this petition appearing to conflict with another one of same date, which will be cited further along.

6. For application of some form of violent death to neighbor who threw brick at family cat, whilst the same was serenading. Reserved for consideration and compromise because of conflict with a prayer of even date to be cited further along.

7. To "damn the missionary cause." Reserved also—as above.

8. To increase December profits of $22,230 to $45,000 for January, and perpetuate a proportionate monthly increase thereafter—"which will satisfy you." The prayer granted; the added remark accepted with reservations.

9. For cyclone, to destroy the works and fill up the mine of the North Pennsylvania Co. NOTE: Cyclones are not kept in stock in the winter season. A reliable article of fire-damp can be furnished upon application.

Especial note is made of the above list, they being of particular moment. The 298 remaining supplications classifiable under the head of Special Providences, Schedule A, for week ending 19th, are granted in a body, except that 3 of the 32 cases requiring immediate death have been modified to incurable disease.

This completes the week's invoice of petitions known to this office under the technical designation of Secret Supplications of the Heart, and which, for a reason which may suggest itself, always receive our first and especial attention.

The remainder of the week's invoice falls under the head of what we term Public Prayers, in which classification we place prayers uttered in Prayer Meeting, Sunday School, Class Meeting, Family Worship, etc. These kinds of prayers have value according to classification of Christian uttering them. By rule of this office, Christians are divided into two grand classes, to wit: (1) Professing Christians; (2) Professional Christians. These, in turn, are minutely subdivided and classified by Size, Species, and Family; and finally, Standing is determined by carats, the minimum being 1, the maximum 1,000.

As per balance sheet for quarter ending Dec. 31st, 1847, you stood classified as follows:

Grand Classification: Professing Christian.

Size: one-fourth of maximum.

Species: Human-Spiritual.

Family: A of the Elect, Division 16.

Standing: 322 carats fine.

As per balance sheet for quarter just ended—that is to say, forty years later—you stand classified as follows:

Grand Classification: Professional Christian.

Size: six one-hundredths of maximum.

Species: Human-Animal.

Family: W of the Elect, Division 1547.

Standing: 3 carats fine.

I have the honor to call your attention to the fact that you seem to have deteriorated.

To resume report upon your Public Prayers—with the side remark that in order to encourage Christians of your grade and of approximate grades, it is the custom of this office to grant many things to them which would not be granted to Christians of a higher grade—partly because they would not be asked for:

Prayer for weather mercifully tempered to the needs of the poor and the naked. Denied. This was a Prayer-Meeting prayer. It conflicts with Item 1 of this report, which was a Secret Supplication of the Heart. By a rigid rule of this office, certain sorts of Public Prayers of Professional Christians are forbidden to take precedence of Secret Supplications of the Heart.

Prayer for better times and plentier food "for the hard-handed son of toil whose patient and exhausting labors make comfortable the homes, and pleasant the ways, of the more fortunate, and entitle him to our vigilant and effective protection from the wrongs and injustices which grasping avarice would do him, and to the tenderest offices of our grateful hearts." Prayer-Meeting prayer. Refused. Conflicts with Secret Supplication of the Heart No. 2.

Prayer "that such as in any way obstruct our preferences may be generously blessed, both themselves and their families, we here calling our hearts to witness that in their worldly prosperity we are spiritually blessed, and our joys made perfect." Prayer-Meeting prayer. Refused. Conflicts with Secret Supplications of the Heart Nos. 3 and 4.

"Oh, let none fall heir to the pains of perdition through words or acts of ours." Family Worship. Received fifteen minutes in advance of Secret Supplication of the Heart No. 5, with which it distinctly conflicts. It is suggested that one or the other of these prayers be withdrawn, or both of them modified.

"Be mercifully inclined toward all who would do us offense in our persons or our property." Includes man who threw brick at cat. Family Prayer. Received some minutes in advance of No. 6, Secret Supplications of the Heart. Modification suggested, to reconcile discrepancy.

"Grant that the noble missionary cause, the most precious labor entrusted to the hands of men, may spread and prosper without let or limit in all heathen lands that do as yet reproach us with their spiritual darkness." Uninvited prayer shoved in at meeting of American Board. Received nearly half a day in advance of No. 7, Secret Supplications of the Heart. This office takes no stock in missionaries, and is not connected in any way with the American Board. We should like to grant one of these prayers, but cannot grant both. It is suggested that the American Board one be withdrawn.

This office desires for the twentieth time to call urgent attention to your remark appended to No. 8. It is a chestnut.

Of the 464 specifications contained in your Public Prayers for the week, and not previously noted in this report, we grant 2, and deny the rest. To wit: Granted, (1) "that the clouds may continue to perform their office; (2) and the sun his." It was the divine purpose anyhow; it will gratify you to know that you have not disturbed it. Of the 462 details refused, 61 were uttered in Sunday School. In this connection I must once more remind you that we grant no Sunday School Prayers of Professional Christians of the classification technically known in this office as the John Wanamaker grade. We merely enter them as "words," and they count to his credit according to number uttered within certain limits of time; 3,000 per quarter-minute required, or no score; 4,200 in a possible 5,000 is a quite common Sunday School score, among experts, and counts the same as two hymns and a bouquet furnished by young ladies in the assassin's cells, execution morning. Your remaining 401 details count for wind only. We bunch them and use them for head winds in retarding the ships of improper people, but it takes so many of them to make an impression that we cannot allow anything for their use.

I desire to add a word of my own to this report. When certain sorts of people do a sizable good deed, we credit them up a thousand-fold more for it than we would in the case of a better man—on account of the strain. You stand far away above your classification record here, because of certain self-sacrifices of yours which greatly exceed what could have been expected of you. Years ago, when you were worth only $100,-000, and sent $2 to your impoverished cousin the widow when she appealed to you for help, there were many in heaven who were not able to believe it, and many more who believed that the money was counterfeit. Your character went up many degrees when it was shown that these suspicions were unfounded. A year or two later, when you sent the poor girl $4 in answer to another appeal, everybody believed it, and you were all the talk here for days together. Two years later you sent $6, upon supplication, when the widow's youngest child died, and that act made perfect your good fame. Everybody in heaven said, "Have you heard about Abner?"—for you are now affectionately called Abner here. Your increasing donation, every two or three years, has kept your name on all lips, and warm in all hearts. All heaven watches you Sundays, as you drive to church in your handsome carriage; and when your hand retires from the contribution plate, the glad shout is heard even to the ruddy walls of remote Sheol, "Another nickel from Abner!"

But the climax came a few days ago, when the widow wrote and said she could get a school in a far village to teach if she had $50 to get herself and her two surviving children over the long journey; and you counted up last month's clear profit from your three coal mines—$22,230—and added to it the certain profit for the current month—$45,000 and a possible fifty—and then got down your pen and your checkbook and mailed her *fifteen whole dollars!* Ah, heaven bless and keep you forever and ever, generous heart! There was not a dry eye in the realms of bliss; and amidst the hand-shakings, and embracings, and praisings, the decree was thundered forth from the shining mount, that this deed should outhonor all the historic self-sacrifices of men and angels, and be recorded by itself upon a page of its own, for that the strain of it upon you had been heavier and bitterer than the strain it costs ten thousand martyrs to yield up their lives at the fiery stake; and all said, "What is the giving up of life, to a noble soul, or to ten thousand noble souls, compared with the giving up of fifteen dollars out of the greedy grip of the meanest white man that ever lived on the face of the earth?"

And it was a true word. And Abraham, weeping, shook out the contents of his bosom and pasted the eloquent label there, "RESERVED"; and Peter, weeping, said, "He shall be received with a torchlight procession when he comes"; and then all heaven boomed, and was glad you were going there. And so was hell.

[Signed]
THE RECORDING ANGEL [SEAL]

By command

A Cat-Tale

My little girls—Susy, aged eight, and Clara, six—often require me to help them go to sleep, nights, by telling them original tales. They think my tales are better than paregoric, and quicker. While I talk, they make comments and ask questions, and we have a pretty good time. I thought maybe other little people might like to try one of my narcotics—so I offer this one.

—M.T.

ONCE there was a noble big cat, whose Christian name was Catasauqua—because she lived in that region—but she did not have any surname, because she was a short-tailed cat—being a Manx—and did not need one. It is very just and becoming in a long-tailed cat to have a surname, but it would be very ostentatious, and even dishonorable, in a Manx. Well, Catasauqua had a beautiful family of catlings; and they were of different colors, to harmonize with their characters. Cattaraugus, the eldest, was white, and he had high impulses and a pure heart; Catiline, the youngest, was black, and he had a self-seeking nature, his motives were nearly always base, he was truculent and insincere. He was vain and foolish, and often said he would rather be what he was, and live like a bandit, yet have none above him, than be a cat-'o-nine-tails and eat with the King. He hated his harmless and unoffending little catercousins, and frequently drove them from his presence with imprecations, and at times even resorted to violence.

SUSY: What are catercousins, Papa?

Quarter-cousins—it is so set down in the big dictionary. You observe I refer to it every now and then. This is because I do not wish to make any mistakes, my purpose being to instruct as well as entertain. Whenever I use a word which you do not understand, speak up and I will look and find out what it means. But do not interrupt me except for cause, for I am always excited when I am erecting history, and want to get on. Well, one day Catasauqua met with a misfortune; her house burned down. It was the very day after it had been in-sured for double its value, too—how singular! Yes, and how lucky! This often happens. It teaches us that mere loading a house down with insurance isn't going to save it. Very well, Catasauqua took the insurance money and built a new house; and a much better one, too; and what is more, she had money left to add a gaudy concatenation of extra improvements with. Oh, I tell you! What she didn't know about catallactics no other cat need ever try to acquire.

CLARA: What is catallactics, Papa?

The dictionary intimates, in a nebulous way, that it is a sort of demi-synonym for the science commonly called political economy.

CLARA: Thank you, Papa.

Yes, behind the house she constructed a splendid large catadrome, and enclosed it with a caterwaul about nine feet high, and in the center was a spacious grass plot where—

CLARA: What is a catadrome, Papa?

I will look. Ah, it is a race course; I thought it was a ten-pin alley. But no matter; in fact, it is all the better; for cats do not play ten-pins, when they are feeling well, but they *do* run races, you know; and the spacious grass plot was for cat fights, and other free exhibitions; and for ball games—three-cornered cat, and all that sort of thing; a lovely spot, lovely. Yes, indeed; it had a hedge of dainty little catkins around it, and right in the center was a splendid great categorematic in full leaf, and—

SUSY: What is a categorematic, Papa?

I think it's a kind of a shade tree, but I'll look. No—I was mistaken; it is a word: "a word which is capable of being employed by itself as a term."

SUSY: Thank you, Papa.

Don't mention it. Yes, you see, it wasn't a shade tree; the good Catasauqua didn't know that, else she wouldn't have planted it right there in the way; you can't run over a word like that, you know, and not cripple yourself more or less. Now don't forget that definition, it may come in handy to you some day—there is no telling—life is full of vicissitudes. Always remember, a categorematic is a word which a cat can use by herself as a term; but she mustn't try to use it along with another cat, for that is not the idea. Far from it. We have authority for it, you see—Mr. Webster; and he is dead, too, besides. It would be a noble good thing if his dictionary was, too. But that is too much to expect. Yes; well, Catasauqua filled her house with internal improvements—catcalls in every room, and they are Oh, ever so much handier than bells; and catamounts to mount the stairs with, instead of those troublesome elevators which are always getting out of order; and civet cats in the kitchen, in place of the ordinary sieves, which you can't ever sift anything with, in a satisfactory way; and a couple of tidy ash cats to clean out the stove and keep it in order; and —catenated on the roof—an alert and cultivated polecat to watch the flagpole and keep the banner a-flying. Ah, yes—such was Catasauqua's country residence; and she named it Kamscatka—after her dear native land far away.

CLARA: What is catenated, Papa?

Chained, my child. The polecat was attached by a chain to some object upon the roof contiguous to the flagpole. This was to retain him in his position.

CLARA: Thank you, Papa.

The front garden was a spectacle of sublime and bewildering magnificence. A stately row of flowering catalpas stretched from the front door clear to the gate, wreathed from stem to stern with the delicate tendrils and shining scales of the cat's-foot ivy, whilst ever and anon the enchanted eye wondered from congeries of lordly cattails and kindred catapetalous blooms too deep for utterance, only to encounter the still more entrancing vision of catnip without number and without price, and swoon away in ecstasy unutterable, under the blissful intoxication of its too, too fragrant breath!

BOTH CHILDREN: Oh, how lovely!

You may well say it. Few there be that shall look upon the like again. Yet was not this all; for hither to the north boiled the majestic cataract in unimaginable grandiloquence, and thither to the south sparkled the gentle catadupe in serene and incandescent tranquillity, whilst far and near the halcyon brooklet flowed between!

BOTH CHILDREN: Oh, how sweet! What is a catadupe, Papa?

Small waterfall, my darlings. Such is Webster's belief. All things being in readiness for the housewarming, the widow sent out her invitations, and then proceeded with her usual avocations. For Catasauqua was a widow—sorrow cometh to us all. The husband-cat—Catullus was his name—was no more. He was of a lofty character, brave to rashness, and almost incredibly unselfish. He gave eight of his lives for his country, reserving only one for himself. Yes, the banquet having been ordered, the good Catasauqua tuned up for the customary morning-song, accompanying herself on the catarrh, and her little ones joined in.

These were the words:

> There was a little cat,
> And she caught a little rat,
> Which she dutifully rendered to her mother,
> Who said "Bake him in a pie,
> For his flavor's rather high—
> Or confer him on the poor, if you'd druther."

Catasauqua sang soprano, Catiline sang tenor, Cattaraugus sang bass. It was exquisite melody; it would make your hair stand right up.

Susy: Why, Papa, I didn't know cats could sing.

Oh, can't they, though! Well, these could. Cats are packed full of music—just as full as they can hold; and when they die, people remove it from them and sell it to the fiddle-makers. Oh, yes indeed. Such is Life.

Susy: Oh, here is a picture! Is it a picture of the music, Papa?

Only the eye of prejudice could doubt it, my child.

SUSY: Did you draw it, Papa?

I am indeed the author of it.

SUSY: How wonderful! What is a picture like this called, Papa?

A work of art, my child. There—do not hold it so close; prop it up on the chair, three steps away; now then—that is right; you see how much better and stronger the expression is than when it is close by. It is because some of this picture is drawn in perspective.

CLARA: Did you always know how to draw, Papa?

Yes. I was born so. But of course I could not draw at first as well as I can now. These things require study and practice. Mere talent is not sufficient. It takes a person a long time to get so he can draw a picture like this.

CLARA: How long did it take you, Papa?

Many years—thirty years, I reckon. Off and on—for I did not devote myself exclusively to art. Still, I have had a great deal of practice. Ah, practice is the great thing! It accomplishes wonders. Before I was twenty-five, I had got so I could draw a cork as well as anybody that ever was. And many a time I have drawn a blank in a lottery. Once I drew a check that wouldn't go; and after the war I tried to draw a pension, but this was too ambitious. However, the most gifted must fail sometimes. Do you observe those things that are sticking up, in this picture? They are not bones, they are paws; it is very hard to express the difference between bones and paws, in a picture.

SUSY: Which is Cattaraugus, Papa?

The little pale one that almost has the end of his mother's tail in his mouth.

SUSY: But, Papa, that tail is not right. You know Catasauqua was a Manx, and had a short one.

It is a just remark, my child; but a long tail was necessary, here, to express a certain passion, the passion of joy. Therefore the insertion of a long tail is permissible; it is called a poetic license. You cannot express the passion of joy with a short tail. Nor even extraordinary excitement. You notice that Cattaraugus is brilliantly excited; now nearly all of that verve, spirit, élan, is owing to his tail; yet if I had been false to art to be true to Nature, you would see there nothing but a poor little stiff and emotionless stump on that cat that would have cast a coldness over the whole scene; yet Cattaraugus was a Manx, like his mother, and had hardly any more tail than a rabbit. Yes, in art, the office of the tail is to express feeling; so,

if you wish to portray a cat in repose, you will always succeed
better by leaving out the tail. Now here is a striking illustration
of the very truth which I am trying to impress upon you. I
proposed to draw a cat recumbent and in repose; but just as I
had finished the front end of her, she got up and began to
gaze passionately at a bird and wriggle her tail in a most
expressively wistful way. I had to finish her with that end
standing, and the other end lying. It greatly injures the picture.
For, you see, it confuses two passions together—the passion of
standing up, and the passion of lying down. These are incom-
patible; and they convey a bad effect to the picture by rendering it unrestful to the eye. In my opinion a cat in a picture
ought to be doing one thing or the other; lying down or standing up, but not both. I ought to have laid this one down again,
and put a brick or something on her; but I did not think of it
at the time. Let us now separate these conflicting passions in
this cat, so that you can see each by itself, and the more easily
study it. Lay your hand on the picture, to where I have made
those dots, and cover the rear half of it from sight—now you
observe how reposeful the front end is. Very well; now lay
your hand on the front end and cover it from sight—do you
observe the eager wriggle in that tail? It is a wriggle which
only the presence of a bird can inspire.

SUSY: You must know a wonderful deal, Papa.

I have that reputation—in Europe; but here the best minds
think I am superficial. However, I am content; I make no
defense; my pictures show what I am.

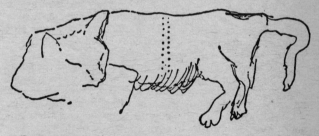

SUSY: Papa, I should think you would take pupils.

No, I have no desire for riches. Honest poverty and a conscience torpid through virtuous inaction are more to me than
corner lots and praise.

But to resume. The morning-song being over, Catasauqua

told Catiline and Cattaraugus to fetch their little books, and she would teach them how to spell.

BOTH CHILDREN: Why, Papa! Do cats have books?

Yes, catechisms. Just so. Facts are stubborn things. After lesson, Catasauqua gave Catiline and Cattaraugus some rushes, so that they could earn a little circus-money by building cat's cradles, and at the same time amuse themselves and not miss her; then she went to the kitchen and dining room to inspect the preparations for the banquet.

The moment her back was turned, Catiline put down his work and got out his catpipe for a smoke.

SUSY: Why, how naughty!

Thou hast well spoken. It was disobedience; and disobedience is the flagship of the fleet of sin. The gentle Cattaraugus sighed and said: "For shame, Catiline! How often has our dear mother told you not to do that! Ah, how can you thus disregard the commandments of the author of your being?"

SUSY: Why, what beautiful language, for such a little thing, wasn't it, Papa?

Ah, yes, indeed. That was the kind of cat he was—cultivated, you see. He had sat at the feet of Rollo's mother; and in the able "Franconia Series" he had not failed to observe how harmoniously gigantic language and a microscopic topic go together. Catiline heard his brother through, and then replied with the contemptuous ejaculation: "S'scat!"

It means the same that Shakespeare means when he says, "Go to." Nevertheless, Catiline's conscience was not at rest. He murmured something about Where was the harm, since his mother would never know? But Cattaraugus said, sweetly but sadly, "Alas, if we but do the right under restraint of authoritative observance, where then is the merit?"

SUSY: How good he was!

Monumentally so. The more we contemplate his character, the more sublime it appears. But Catiline, who was coarse and worldly, hated all lofty sentiments, and especially such as were stated in choice and lofty terms; he wished to resent this one, yet compelled himself to hold his peace; but when Cattaraugus said it over again, partly to enjoy the sound of it, but mainly for his brother's good, Catiline lost his patience, and said, "Oh, take a walk!"

Yet he still felt badly; for he knew he was doing wrong. He began to pretend he did not know it was against the rule to smoke his catpipe; but Cattaraugus, without an utterance, lifted an accusing paw toward the wall, where, among the illuminated mottoes, hung this one:

"NO SMOKING. STRICTLY PROHIBITED."

Catiline turned pale; and, murmuring in a broken voice, "I am undone—forgive me, Brother," laid the fatal catpipe aside and burst into tears.

CLARA: Poor thing! It was cruel, wasn't it, Papa?

SUSY: Well but he oughtn't to done so, in the first place. Cattaraugus wasn't to blame.

CLARA: Why, Susy! If Catiline didn't know he wasn't allowed—

SUSY: Catiline did know it—Cattaraugus told him so; and besides, Catiline—

CLARA: Cattaraugus only told Catiline that if—

SUSY: Why, Clara! Catiline didn't need for Cattaraugus to say one single—

Oh, hold on! It's all a mistake! Come to look in the dictionary, we are proceeding from false premises. The Unabridged says a catpipe is "a squeaking instrument used in play-houses to condemn plays." So you see it wasn't a pipe to smoke, after all; Catiline couldn't smoke it; therefore it follows that he was simply pretending to smoke it, to stir up his brother, that's all.

SUSY: But, Papa, Catiline might as well smoke as stir up his brother.

CLARA: Susy, you don't like Catiline, and so whatever he does, it don't suit you, it ain't right; and he is only a little fellow, anyway.

SUSY: I don't approve of Catiline, but I like him well enough; I only say—

CLARA: What is approve?

SUSY: Why it's as if you did something, and I said it was all right. So I think he might as well smoke as stir up his brother. Isn't it so, Papa?

Looked at from a strictly mathematical point of view, I don't know, but it is a case of six-in-one-and-half-a-dozen-in-the-other. Still, our business is mainly with the historical facts; if we only get them right, we can leave posterity to take care of the moral aspects of the matter. To resume the thread of the narrative, when Cattaraugus saw that Catiline had not been smoking at all, but had only been making believe, and this too with the avowed object of fraternal aggravation, he was deeply hurt; and by his heat was beguiled into recourse to that bit'er weapon, sarcasm; saying, "The Roman Catiline would have betrayed his foe; it was left to the Catasauquian to refine upon the model and betray his friend."

"Oh, a gaudy speech!—and very erudite and swell!" retorted Catiline, derisively, "but just a *little* catachrestic."

SUSY: What is catachrestic, Papa?

"Farfetched," the dictionary says. The remark stung Cattaraugus to the quick, and he called Catiline a catapult; this infuriated Catiline beyond endurance, and he threw down the gauntlet and called Cattaraugus a catso. No cat will stand that; so at it they went. They spat and clawed and fought until they dimmed away and finally disappeared in a flying fog of cat fur.

CLARA: What is a catso, Papa?

"A base fellow, a rogue, a cheat," says the dictionary. When the weather cleared, Cattaraugus, ever ready to acknowledge a fault, whether committed by himself or another, said, "I was wrong, brother—forgive me. A cat may err—to err is cattish; but toward even a foreigner, even a wildcat, catacaustic remark is in ill taste; how much more so, then, when a brother is the target! Yes, Catiline, I was wrong; I deeply regret the circumstance. Here is my hand—let us forget the dark o'erclouded past in the bright welkin of the present, consecrating ourselves anew to its nobler lessons, and sacrificing ourselves yet again, and forever if need be, to the thrice-armed beacon that binds them in one!"

SUSY: He was a splendid talker, wasn't he, Papa? Papa, what is catacaustic?

Well, a catacaustic remark is a bitter, malicious remark—a sort of a—sort of—or a kind of a—well, let's look in the dictionary; that is cheaper. Oh, yes, here it is: "CATACAUSTIC, n; a caustic curve formed by reflection of light." Oh, yes, that's it.

SUSY: Well, Papa, what does *that* mean?

Cooper's Prose Style

YOUNG GENTLEMAN: In studying Cooper you will find it profitable to study him in detail—word by word, sentence by sentence. For every sentence of his is interesting. Interesting because of its make-up; its peculiar make-up, its original make-up. Let us examine a sentence or two, and see. Here is a passage from Chapter XI of *The Last of the Mohicans*, one of the most famous and most admired of Cooper's books:

Notwithstanding the swiftness of their flight, one of the Indians had found an opportunity to strike a straggling fawn with an arrow, and had borne the more preferable fragments of the victim, patiently on his shoulders, to the stopping-place. Without any aid from the science of cookery, he was immediately employed, in common with his fellows, in gorging himself with this digestible sustenance. Magua alone sat apart, without participating in the revolting meal, and apparently buried in the deepest thought.

This little paragraph is full of matter for reflection and inquiry. The remark about the swiftness of the flight was unnecessary, as it was merely put in to forestall the possible objection of some overparticular reader that the Indian couldn't have found the needed "opportunity" while fleeing swiftly. The reader would not have made that objection. He would care nothing about having that small matter explained and justified. But that is Cooper's way; frequently he will explain and justify little things that do not need it and then make up for this by as frequently failing to explain important ones that do need it. For instance he allowed that astute and cautious person, Deerslayer-Hawkeye, to throw his rifle heedlessly down and leave it lying on the ground where some hostile Indians would presently be sure to find it—a rifle prized by that person above all things else in the earth—and the reader gets no word of explanation of that strange act. There was a reason, but it wouldn't bear exposure. Cooper meant to get a fine dramatic effect out of the finding of the rifle by the Indians, and he accomplished this at the happy time; but all the same, Hawkeye could have hidden the rifle in a quarter of a minute where the Indians could not have found it. Cooper couldn't think of any way to explain why Hawkeye didn't do that, so he just shirked the difficulty and did not explain at all. In another place Cooper allowed Heyward to shoot at an Indian with a pistol that wasn't loaded—and grants us not a word of explanation as to how the man did it.

No, the remark about the swiftness of their flight was not necessary; neither was the one which said that the Indian found an opportunity; neither was the one which said he struck the fawn; neither was the one which explained that it was a "straggling" fawn; neither was the one which said the striking was done with an arrow; neither was the one which said the Indian bore the "fragments"; nor the remark that they were preferable fragments; nor the remark that they were more preferable fragments; nor the explanation that they were fragments of the "victim"; nor the overparticular explanation that specifies the Indian's "shoulders" as the part of him that supported the fragments; nor the statement that the Indian bore the fragments patiently. None of those details has any value. We don't care what the Indian struck the fawn with; we don't care whether it was a struggling fawn or an unstruggling one; we don't care which fragments the Indian saved; we don't care why he saved the "more" preferable ones when the merely preferable ones would have amounted to just the same thing and couldn't have been told from the more preferable ones by anybody, dead or alive; we don't care whether the Indian carried them on his shoulders or in his handkerchief; and finally, we don't care whether he carried them patiently or struck for higher pay and shorter hours. We are indifferent to that Indian and all his affairs.

There was only one fact in that long sentence that was worth stating, and it could have been squeezed into these few words—and with advantage to the narrative, too: "During the flight one of the Indians had killed a fawn and he brought it into camp."

You will notice that "During the flight one of the Indians had killed a fawn and he brought it into camp," is more straightforward and business-like, and less mincing and smirky, than it is to say, "Notwithstanding the swiftness of their flight, one of the Indians had found an opportunity to strike a straggling fawn with an arrow, and had borne the more preferable fragments of the victim, patiently on his shoulders, to the stopping-place." You will notice that the form "During the flight one of the Indians had killed a fawn and he brought it into camp" holds up its chin and moves to the front with the steady stride of a grenadier, whereas the form "Notwithstanding the swiftness of their flight, one of the Indians had found an opportunity to strike a straggling fawn with an arrow, and had borne the more preferable fragments of the victim, patiently on his shoulders, to the stopping-place" simpers along with an airy, complacent, monkey-with-a-parasol gait which is not suited to the transportation of raw meat.

I beg to remind you that an author's way of setting forth a matter is called his Style, and that an author's style is a main part of his equipment for business. The style of some authors has variety in it, but Cooper's style is remarkable for the absence of this feature. Cooper's style is always grand and stately and noble. Style may be likened to an army, the author to its general, the book to the campaign. Some authors proportion an attacking force to the strength or weakness, the importance or unimportance, of the object to be attacked; but Cooper doesn't. It doesn't make any difference to Cooper whether the object of attack is a hundred thousand men or a cow; he hurls his entire force against it. He comes thundering down with all his battalions at his back, cavalry in the van, artillery on the flanks, infantry massed in the middle, forty bands braying, a thousand banners streaming in the wind; and whether the object be an army or a cow you will see him come marching sublimely in, at the end of the engagement, bearing the more preferable fragments of the victim patiently on his shoulders, to the stopping-place. Cooper's style is grand, awful, beautiful; but it is sacred to Cooper, it is his very own, and no student of the Veterinary College of Arizona will be allowed to filch it from him.

In one of his chapters Cooper throws an ungentle slur at one Gamut because he is not exact enough in his choice of words. But Cooper has that failing himself, as remarked in our first lecture. If the Indian had "struck" the fawn with a brick, or with a club, or with his fist, no one could find fault with the word used. And one cannot find much fault when he strikes it with an arrow; still it sounds affected, and it might have been a little better to lean to simplicity and say he shot it with an arrow.

"Fragments" is well enough, perhaps, when one is speaking of the parts of a dismembered deer, yet it hasn't just exactly the right sound—and sound is something; in fact sound is a good deal. It makes the difference between good music and poor music, and it can sometimes make the difference between good literature and indifferent literature. "Fragments" sounds all right when we are talking about the wreckage of a breakable thing that has been smashed; it also sounds all right when applied to cat's meat; but when we use it to describe large hunks and chunks like the fore- and hindquarters of a fawn, it grates upon the fastidious ear.

"Without any aid from the science of cookery, he was immediately employed, in common with his fellows, in gorging himself with this digestible sustenance."

This was a mere statistic; just a mere cold, colorless statistic; yet you see Cooper has made a chromo out of it. To use another figure, he has clothed a humble statistic in flowing, voluminous and costly raiment, whereas both good taste and economy suggest that he ought to have saved these splendors for a king, and dressed the humble statistic in a simple breechclout. Cooper spent twenty-four words here on a thing not really worth more than eight. We will reduce the statistic to its proper proportions and state it in this way:

"He and the others ate the meat raw."

"Digestible sustenance" is a handsome phrase, but it was out of place there, because we do not know these Indians or care for them; and so it cannot interest us to know whether the meat was going to agree with them or not. Details which do not assist a story are better left out.

"Magua alone sat apart, without participating in the revolting meal" is a statement which we understand, but that is our merit, not Cooper's. Cooper is not clear. He does not say who it is that is revolted by the meal. It is really Cooper himself, but there is nothing in the statement to indicate that it isn't Magua. Magua is an Indian and likes raw meat.

The word "alone" could have been left out and space saved. It has no value where it is.

I must come back with some frequency, in the course of these lectures, to the matter of Cooper's inaccuracy as an Observer. In this way I shall hope to persuade you that it is well to look at a thing carefully before you try to describe it; but I shall rest you between times with other matters and thus try to avoid overfatiguing you with that detail of our theme. In *The Last of the Mohicans* Cooper gets up a stirring "situation" on an island flanked by great cataracts—a lofty island with steep sides—a sort of tongue which projects downstream from the midst of the divided waterfall. There are caverns in this mass of rock, and a party of Cooper people hide themselves in one of these to get away from some hostile Indians. There is a small exit at each end of this cavern. These exits are closed with blankets and the light excluded. The exploring hostiles back themselves up against the blankets and rave and rage in a blood-curdling way, but they are Cooper Indians and of course fail to discover the blankets; so they presently go away baffled and disappointed. Alice, in her gratitude for this deliverance, flings herself on her knees to return thanks. The darkness in there must have been pretty solid; yet if we may believe Cooper, it was a darkness which could not have been told from daylight; for here are some nice details which were visible in it:

Both Heyward and the more tempered Cora witnessed the act of involuntary emotion with powerful sympathy, the former secretly believing that piety had never worn a form so lovely as it had now assumed in the youthful person of Alice. Her eyes were radiant with the glow of grateful feelings; the flush of her beauty was again seated on her cheeks, and her whole soul seemed ready and anxious to pour out its thanksgivings, through the medium of her eloquent features. But when her lips moved, the words they should have uttered appeared frozen by some new and sudden chill. Her bloom gave place to the paleness of death; her soft and melting eyes grew hard, and seemed contracting with horror; while those hands which she had raised, clasped in each other, towards heaven, dropped in horizontal lines before her, the fingers pointed forward in convulsed motion.

It is a case of strikingly inexact observation. Heyward and the more tempered Cora could not have seen the half of it in the dark that way.

I must call your attention to certain details of this work of art which invite particular examination. "Involuntary" is surplusage, and violates Rule 14.* All emotion is involuntary when genuine, and then the qualifying term is not needed; a qualifying term is needed only when the emotion is pumped-up and

* Of nineteen rules "governing literary art in the domain of romantic fiction," which Mark Twain had listed in "Fenimore Cooper's Literary Offenses" (in *How to Tell a Story*, 1897), and of which, he claimed, Cooper's *Deerslayer* violated eighteen. The fourteenth is "Eschew surplusage." [B. DV.]

ungenuine. "Secretly" is surplusage, too; because Heyward was not believing out loud, but all to himself; and a person cannot believe a thing all to himself without doing it privately. I do not approve of the word "seated" to describe the process of locating a flush. No one can seat a flush. A flush is not a deposit on an exterior surface, it is a something which squshes out from within.

I cannot approve of the word "new." If Alice had had an old chill, formerly, it would be right to distinguish this one from that one by calling this one the new chill; but she had not had any old chill, this one was the only chill she had had, up till now, and so the tacit reference to an old anterior chill is unwarranted and misleading. And I do not altogether like the phrase "while those hands which she had raised." It seems to imply that she had some other hands—some other ones which she had put on the shelf a minute so as to give her a better chance to raise these ones; but it is not true; she had only the one pair. The phrase is in the last degree misleading. But I like to see her extend these ones in front of her and work the fingers. I think that that is a very good effect. And it would have almost doubled the effect if the more tempered Cora had done it some, too.

A Cooper Indian who has been washed is a poor thing, and commonplace; it is the Cooper Indian in his paint that thrills. Cooper's extra words are Cooper's paint—his paint, his feathers, his tomahawk, his warwhoop.

In the two-thirds of a page elsewhere referred to, wherein Cooper scored 114 literary transgressions out of a possible 115, he appears before us with all his things on. As follows; the italics are mine—they indicate violations of Rule 14:

In a minute he was once more fastened to the tree, a *helpless object of any insult or wrong that might be offered. So eagerly did every one now act, that nothing was said.* The fire was immediately lighted *in the pile, and the end of all was anxiously expected.*

It was not the intention of the Hurons *absolutely* to destroy *the life* of their victim *by means of* fire. They designed merely to put his *physical* fortitude to the severest proofs it could endure, short of that extremity. In the end, they fully intended to carry his scalp into their village, but it was their wish first to break down his resolution, and to reduce him to *the level of* a complaining sufferer. With this view, *the pile of brush and branches* had been placed at a *proper distance,*

or one at which it was thought the heat would soon become intolerable, though it might not be immediately dangerous. As often happened, however, on these occasions, this distance had been miscalculated, and the flames began to wave their forked tongues in a
proximity to the face of the victim that would have proved fatal in
another instant had not Hetty rushed through the crowd, armed with
a stick, and scattered the blazing pile in a dozen directions. More than
one hand was raised to strike the presumptuous intruder to the earth;
but the chiefs prevented the blows by reminding their irritated fol-
lowers of the state of her mind. Hetty, herself, was insensible to the
risk she ran; but, as soon as she had performed this bold act, she stood
looking about her in frowning resentment, as if to rebuke the crowd
of attentive savages for their cruelty.

"God bless you, dearest sister, for that brave and ready act," murmured Judith, herself unnerved so much as to be incapable of exer-
tion; "Heaven itself has sent you on its holy errand."

Number of words, 320; necessary ones, 220: words wasted
by the generous spendthrift, 100.

In our day those 100 unnecessary words would have to come
out. We will take them out presently and make the episode
approximate the modern requirement in the matter of com-
pression.

If we may consider each unnecessary word in Cooper's report
of that barbecue a separate and individual violation of Rule 14,
then that rule is violated 100 times in that report. Other rules
are violated in it. Rule 12, 2 instances; Rule 13, 5 instances;
Rule 15, 1 instance; Rule 16, 2 instances; Rule 17, 1 or 2 little
instances; the report in its entirety is an offense against Rule
18—also against Rule 16. Total score, about 114 violations of
the laws of literary art out of a possible 115.*

Let us now bring forward the report again, with the most of
the unnecessary words knocked out. By departing from Cooper's style and manner, all the facts could be put into 150 words,
and the effects heightened at the same time—this is manifest,
of course—but that would not be desirable. We must stick to
Cooper's language as closely as we can:

* Rule 12: "[The author shall] *Say* what he is proposing to say, not
merely come near it."
  Rule 13: "Use the right word, not its second cousin."
  Rule 15: "Not omit necessary details."
  Rule 16: "Avoid slovenliness of form."
  Rule 17: "Use good grammar."
  Rule 18: "Employ a simple and straightforward style." [B. DV.]

In a minute he was once more fastened to the tree. The fire was immediately lighted. It was not the intention of the Hurons to destroy Deerslayer's life by fire; they designed merely to put his fortitude to the severest proofs it could endure short of that extremity. In the end, they fully intended to take his life, but it was their wish first to break down his resolution and reduce him to a complaining sufferer. With this view the pile of brush had been placed at a distance at which it was thought the heat would soon become intolerable, without being immediately dangerous. But this distance had been miscalculated; the fire was so close to the victim that he would have been fatally burned in another instant if Hetty had not rushed through the crowd and scattered the brands with a stick. More than one Indian raised his hand to strike her down, but the chiefs saved her by reminding them of the state of her mind. Hetty herself was insensible to the risk she ran; she stood looking about her in frowning resentment, as if to rebuke the savages for their cruelty.

"God bless you, dear!" cried Judith, "for that brave and ready act. Heaven itself has sent you on its holy errand, and you shall have a chromo."

Number of words, 220—and the facts are all in.

Official Report to the I.I.A.S.
(1909)

A S SECRETARY of the Indianapolis Institute of Applied Science it has been my duty to inquire into the alleged discovery of the North Pole and lay the result of the inquiry before your honorable body.

In pursuance of this duty it has seemed to me sufficient to get the views of Professor Hiram Bledso, a recognized master in Comparative Science and Theology, and stop there.

I asked him if, in his judgment, we should accept the discovery as a thing conclusively established, and go on and celebrate it, along with the other memorable Nines—1609, 1809, and 1909—at the same time displaying, upon a decorated float, a man representing Henry Hudson; upon another float a man representing Robert Fulton, and upon a third float Dr. Frederick Cook in person.

Professor Bledso asked leave to consider the question a few minutes. Then he said, "The answer, yes or no, depends entirely upon the answer to this question: Is it claimed that Dr. Cook's achievement is a Fact, or is it a Miracle?"

"Why so?"

"Because if it is a Miracle, any sort of evidence will answer, but if it is a Fact, proof is necessary."

"Is that the law?"

"Yes. It is absolute. Modifications of it are not permissible. A very pertinent remark has been quoted from the *Westminster Gazette*, which points out that 'the golfer, when he puts in a record round, has to have his card signed, and that there is nobody to sign Dr. Cook's card; there are two Eskimos to vouch for his feat, to be sure, but they were his caddies, and at golf their evidence would not be accepted.' There you have the whole case. If Dr. Cook's feat is put forward as Fact, the evidence of his two caddies is inadequate; if it is put forward as Miracle, one caddy is aplenty."

"Is there really all that difference between Fact and Miracle?"

"Yes, there is history for it—ages of history. There has never been a Miracle that noticeably resembled a Fact. Take an illustration. Mr. Janvier quotes this item from Henry Hudson's log—Hudson wrote it fourteen months before his discovery of the River:

This morning one of our companie looking overboard saw a mermaid, and calling up some of the companie to see her, one more came up and by that time shee was come close to the ships side, looking earnestly on the men. A little after a sea came and overturned her. From the navill upward her backe and breasts were like a womans, but her body as big as one of us. Her skin very white, and long haire hanging down behinde of colour blacke. In her going downe they saw her tayle, which was like the tayle of a porposse, and speckled like a macrell. Their names that saw her were Thomas Hilles and Robert Rayner.

"Observe, to Hudson that was not a Fact, it was a Miracle. How do I know this? Because he believes, on the mere say-so of a couple of sailors. He knows they saw the mermaids, for he doesn't say they thought they saw, he says with convinced positiveness, they saw. Very well. As a Miracle, the sailors' say-so is quite sufficient—indeed, more than sufficient; there isn't a better-grounded Miracle in history. But to Dr. Asher, a recent commentator, who considered that Hudson was registering the incident as a Fact, the evidence was but caddy evidence and quite inadequate. He remarks, 'Probably a seal.' "

"Then the difference—"

"Quite so. The difference between a Miracle and a Fact is exactly the difference between a mermaid and a seal. It could not be better expressed."

"Very well. What do we arrive at, in this North Pole matter? What course is best for the Institute and the Robert Fulton people to pursue?"

"In my judgment, this. If you wish to proceed upon the hypothesis that it is a Miracle, go right along, get your float ready, the evidence is overwhelming. But if you wish to proceed upon the hypothesis that it is a Fact, wait till Cook arrives and has a chance to furnish his evidence in comprehensive detail. It cannot be fair to decide upon a verdict any earlier."

H. J. WALKER,
Secretary

Indianapolis, Sept. 3

The Gorky Incident
(1906)

LET ME resurrect the "York Minster" episode of seventy-five years ago—and enlarge it a little for present purposes. York Minster—such was his nickname—was a native of Tierra del Fuego. He was a likable young fellow, bright, animated, rather handsome, and of a particularly shapely figure. Let him be where he might, his figure was always on exhibition, for he wore not a rag of clothing, except a square of untanned skin between his shoulders. His costume did not make him conspicuous, because it was the costume of his whole nation.

The commander of a British warship fitted York Minster out with Christian clothing, taught him the rudiments of English speech, and took him home over the seas. He became at once an object of great and earnest interest; the public welcomed him, the newspapers were full of him, all ranks offered him their hospitalities. Naturally he was pleased and grateful. Among his invitations was one which took precedence of all the others—the King's ball, at St. James's Palace. He got himself ready for that. For the sake of convenience and comfort he resumed his national costume, thinking no harm; and at 11 P.M., he appeared in the midst of that gorgeous assemblage clad only in his awful innocence and that pathetic shoulder-skin.

Do you know, he emptied that place in two minutes by the watch. Then the guards turned him into the street. When he reached his hotel he was denied admission. The other hotels refused him. It looked as if he was nevermore going to find shelter, but at last he was rescued from his difficulties by compassionate friends.

Then the wise and the unwise began on him in the newspapers, and led him a dance. A friend defended him and explained that York was only following a recognized and perfectly proper custom of his own country and therefore was doing no wrong. Other friends defended him and proved by facts and arguments that the dress customs of Tierra del Fuego were more just and rational than were those of England; and then claimed that since this was the case the English had no right to find fault with this foreigner and inhospitably upbraid him and revile him for what he had done.

All of which was wasted ink, I think. Laws are coldly reasoned out and established upon what the lawmakers believe to be a basis of right. But customs are not. Customs are not enacted, they grow gradually up, imperceptibly and unconsciously, like an oak from its seed. In the fullness of their strength they can stand up straight in front of a world of argument and reasoning, and yield not an inch. We do not know how or when it became custom for women to wear long hair, we only know that in this country it is custom, and that settles it. Maybe it is right, maybe it is wrong—that has nothing to do with the matter; customs do not concern themselves with right or wrong or reason. But they have to be obeyed; one may reason all around them until he is tired, but he must not transgress them, it is sternly forbidden. Women may shave their heads elsewhere, but here they must refrain or take the uncomfortable consequences. Laws are sand, customs are rock. Laws can be evaded and punishment escaped, but an openly transgressed custom brings sure punishment. The penalty may be unfair, unrighteous, illogical, and a cruelty; no matter, it will be inflicted, just the same. Certainly, then, there can be but one wise thing for a visiting stranger to do—find out what the country's customs are, and refrain from offending against them.

The efforts which have been made in Gorky's justification are entitled to all respect because of the magnanimity of the motive back of them, but I think that the ink was wasted. Custom is custom; it is built of brass, boiler iron, granite; facts, reasonings, arguments have no more effect upon it than the idle winds have upon Gibraltar.

However, I must return to York Minster and finish that story. After reflection, he put on his clothes again.

Simplified Spelling

THE first time I was in Egypt a Simplified Spelling epidemic had broken out and the atmosphere was electrical with feeling engendered by the subject. This was four or five thousand years ago—I do not remember just how many thousand it was, for my memory for minor details has suffered some decay in the lapse of years. I am speaking of a former state of existence of mine, perhaps my earliest reincarnation; indeed I think it was the earliest. I had been an angel previously, and I am expecting to be one again—but at the time I speak of I was different.

The Simplifiers had risen in revolt against the hieroglyphics. An uncle of Cadmus who was out of a job had come to Egypt and was trying to introduce the Phoenician alphabet and get it adop·ed in place of the hieroglyphics. He was challenged to sł ow cause, and he did it to the best of his ability. The exhibition and discussion took place in the Temple of Astarte, and I was present. So also was the Simplified Committee, with Croesus as foreman of the Revolt—not a large man physically, but a simplified speller of acknowledged ability. The Simplifiers were few; the Opposition were multitudinous. The Khedive was the main backer of the Revolt, and this magnified its strength and saved it from being insignificant. Among the Simplifiers were many men of learning and distinction, mainly literary men and members of college faculties; but all ranks and conditions of men and all grades of intellect, erudition, and ignorance were represented in the Opposition.

As a rule the speeches on both sides were temperate and courteous, but now and then a speaker weakened his argument with personalities, the Revolters referring to the Opposition as fossils, and the Opposition referring to the Revolters as "those cads," a smart epithet coined out of the name of Uncle Cadmus.

Uncle Cadmus began with an object lesson, with chalk, on a couple of blackboards. On one of them he drew in outline a slender Egyptian in a short skirt, with slim legs and an eagle's head in place of a proper head, and he was carrying a couple of dinner pails, one in each hand. In front of this figure he drew a toothed line like an excerpt from a saw; in front of this he drew three skeleton birds of doubtful ornithological origin; in front of these he drew a partly constructed house, with lean Egyptians fetching materials in wheelbarrows to finish it with; next he put in some more unclassified birds; then a large king, with carpenter's shavings for whiskers and hair; next he put in another king jabbing a mongrel lion with a javelin; he followed this with a picture of a tower, with armed Egyptians projecting out of the top of it and as crowded for room as the cork in a bottle; he drew the opposing army below, fierce of aspect but much out of drawing as regards perspective. They were shooting arrows at the men in the tower, which was poor military judgment because they could have reached up and pulled them out by the scruff of the neck. He followed these pictures with line after line of birds and beasts and scraps of saw-teeth and bunches of men in the customary short frock, some of them doing things, the others waiting for the umpire to call game; and finally his great blackboard was full from top to bottom. Everybody recognized the invocation set forth by the symbols: it was the Lord's Prayer.

It had taken him forty-five minutes to set it down. Then he stepped to the other blackboard and dashed off "Our Father which art in heaven," and the rest of it, in graceful Italian script, spelling the words the best he knew how in those days, and finished it up in four minutes and a half.

It was rather impressive.

He made no comment at the time, but went to a fresh blackboard and wrote upon it in hieroglyphics:

"At this time the King possessed of cavalry 214,580 men and 222,631 horses for their use; of infantry 16,341 squadrons together with an emergency reserve of all arms, consisting of 84,946 men, 321 elephants, 37,264 transportation carts, and 28,954 camels and dromedaries."

It filled the board and cost him twenty-six minutes of time and labor. Then he repeated it on another blackboard in Italian script and Arabic numerals and did it in two minutes and a quarter. Then he said:

"My argument is before you. One of the objections to the hieroglyphics is that it takes the brightest pupil nine years to get the forms and their meanings by heart; it takes the average pupil sixteen years; it takes the rest of the nation all their days to accomplish it—it is a life sentence. This cost of time is much too expensive. It could be employed more usefully in other industries, and with better results.

"If you will renounce the hieroglyphics and adopt written words instead, an advantage will be gained. By you? No, not by you. You have spent your lives in mastering the hieroglyphics, and to you they are simple, and the effect pleasant to the eye, and even beautiful. You are well along in life; it would not be worth your while to acquire the new learning; the aspect of it would be unpleasant to you; you will naturally cling with affection to the pictured records which have become beautiful to you through habit and use, and which are associated in your mind with the moving legends and tales of our venerable past and the great deeds of our fathers, which they have placed before you indestructibly engraved upon stone. But I appeal to you in behalf of the generations which are to follow you, century after century, age after age, cycle after cycle. I pray you consider them and be generous. Lift this heavy burden from their backs. Do not send them toiling and moiling down to the twentieth century still bearing it, still oppressed by it. Let your sons and daughters adopt the words and the alphabet, and go free. To the youngest of them the hieroglyphics have no hallowed associations; the words and the alphabet will not offend their eyes; custom will quickly reconcile them to it, and then they will prefer it—if for no other reason, for the simple reason that they will have had no experience of any method of communication considered by others comelier or better. I pray you let the hieroglyphics go, and thus save millions of years of useless time and labor to fifty generations of posterity that are to follow you.

"Do I claim that the substitute which I am proposing is without defect? No. It has a serious defect. My fellow Revolters are struggling for one thing, and for one thing only—the shortening and simplifying of the spelling. That is to say, they have not gone to the root of the matter—and in my opinion the reform which they are urging is hardly worthwhile. The trouble is not with the spelling; it goes deeper than that; it is with the *alphabet*. There is but one way to scientifically and adequately reform the orthography, and that is by reforming the alphabet; then the orthography will reform itself. What is needed is that each letter of the alphabet shall have a perfectly definite sound, and that this sound shall never be changed or modified without the addition of an accent, or other visible sign, to indicate precisely and exactly the nature of the modification. The Germans have this kind of an alphabet. Every letter of it has a perfectly definite sound, and when that sound is modified an *umlaut* or other sign is added to indicate the precise shade of the modification. The several values of the German letters can be learned by the ordinary child in a few days, and after that, for ninety years, that child can always correctly spell any German word it hears, without ever having been taught to do it by another person, or being obliged to apply to a spelling book for help.

"But the English alphabet is a pure insanity. It can hardly spell any word in the language with any large degree of certainty. When you see the word *chaldron* in an English book no foreigner can guess how to pronounce it; neither can any native. The reader knows that it is pronounced *chaldron*—or *kaldron*, or *kawldron*—but neither he nor his grandmother can tell which is the right way without looking in the dictionary; and when he looks in the dictionary the chances are a hundred to one that the dictionary itself doesn't know which is the right way, but will furnish him all three and let him take his choice. When you find the word *bow* in an English book, standing by itself and without any informing text built around it, there is no American or Englishman alive, nor any dictionary, that can tell you how to pronounce that word. It may mean a gesture of salutation and rhyme with cow; and it may also mean an obsolete military weapon and rhyme with blow. But let us not enlarge upon this. The sillinesses of the English alphabet are quite beyond enumeration. That alphabet consists of nothing whatever except sillinesses. I venture to repeat that whereas the English orthography needs reforming and simplifying, the English alphabet needs it two or three million times more."

Uncle Cadmus sat down, and the Opposition rose and combated his reasonings in the usual way. Those people said that they had always been used to the hieroglyphics; that the hieroglyphics had dear and sacred associations for them; that they loved to sit on a barrel under an umbrella in the brilliant sun of Egypt and spell out the owls and eagles and alligators and saw-teeth, and take an hour and a half to the Lord's Prayer, and weep with romantic emotion at the thought that they had, at most, but eight or ten years between themselves and the grave for the enjoyment of this ecstasy; and that then possibly these Revolters would shove the ancient signs and symbols from the main track and equip the people with a lightning-express reformed alphabet that would leave the hieroglyphic wheelbarrow a hundred thousand miles behind and have not a damned association which could compel a tear, even if tears and diamonds stood at the same price in the market.

Something About Repentance
(1908)

I
T IS curious—the misassociation of certain words. For
instance, the word Repentance. Through want of reflection we associate it exclusively with Sin. We get the notion
early, and keep it always, that we repent of bad deeds only;
whereas we do a formidably large business in repenting of
good deeds which we have done. Often when we repent of a
sin, we do it perfunctorily, from principle, coldly and from the
head; but when we repent of a good deed the repentance comes
hot and bitter and straight from the heart. Often when we repent of a sin, we can forgive ourselves and drop the matter out
of mind; but when we repent of a good deed, we seldom get
peace—we go on repenting to the end. And the repentance is
so perennially young and strong and vivid and vigorous! A great
benefaction conferred with your whole heart upon an ungrate-
ful man—with what immortal persistence and never-cooling
energy do you repent of that! Repentance of a sin is a pale,
poor, perishable thing compared with it.

I am quite sure that the average man is built just as I am;
otherwise I should not be making this revelation of my inside.
I say the average man and stop there; for I am quite certain
that there are people who do not repent of their good deeds
when the return they get for them is treachery and ingratitude.
I think that these few ought to be in heaven; they are in the
way here. In my time I have committed several millions of
sins. Many of them I probably repented of—I do not remember now; others I was partly minded to repent of, but it did
not seem worthwhile; all of them but the recent ones and a
few scattering former ones I have forgotten. In my time I have
done eleven good deeds. I remember all of them, four of them
with crystal clearness. These four I repent of whenever I think
of them—and it is not seldomer than fifty-two times a year. I
repent of them in the same old original furious way, un-
diminished, always. If I wake up away in the night, they are

there, waiting and ready; and they keep me company till the morning. I have not committed any sin that has lasted me like this save one; and have not repented of any sin with the unmodifying earnestness and sincerity with which I have repented of these four gracious and beautiful good deeds.

Possibly you who are reading these paragraphs are of those few who have got mislaid and ought to be in heaven. In that case you will not understand what I have been saying and will have no sympathy with it; but your neighbor will, if he is fifty years old.

From an English Notebook

In 1872 Mark Twain went to England intending to write a book, as Mr. Paine says, about "its people and institutions." For a number of reasons he did not write the book but one of the notebooks which he kept during his visit has been preserved, and these extracts have been taken from it.

B. DV.

I THE ALBERT MEMORIAL

WE drove through Hyde Park, and all of a sudden a magnificent structure burst upon us. We got out and stood gazing at it in mute wonder. It was a tall, ornate pinnacle, pierced with arches and flanked by noble groups of statuary; and this airy, graceful pinnacle was splendid with gilding and richly colored mosaics, from its base to its summit. It was the brightest, freshest, loveliest bit of gigantic jewelry in all this battered and blackened old city. The fascinated sun fondled it, petted it, glorified it. The very railings that enclosed the spacious marble platform it stood upon were sumptuously gilded. At the four corners of these railings, elevated upon great marble pedestals, were four groups of the groups of statuary I have mentioned—and the principal. All clean, and white and new. And all huge, imposing figures. And so perfectly wrought and so happily grouped that from whatever point you examined them they were symmetrical, harmonious, guiltless of blemish. One group represented Asia—a stately female figure seated upon a prostrate elephant, and surrounded by Persians, Chinese, Indian warriors, and an Arab reading the Koran. Another group represented Europe—a woman seated upon a bull, and round about her other female figures typifying England and the States of the Continent. A third group represents America—an Indian woman seated upon a buffalo which is careering through the long prairie grass; and about her are half

137

a dozen figures representing the United States, Canada, South America, and so forth. The fourth group represents Africa— an Egyptian princess seated upon a camel, and surrounded by other typical figures. One cannot convey with words the majesty of these stony creatures—the ease, the dignity, the grace, that sit upon them so royally. And there is no slurring over of anything—every little detail is perfect. The fringes that depend from the camels' covering fall as limp and pliant as if they were woven instead of chiseled; no 'prentice work is visible anywhere.

We approached and entered the enclosure and mingled with the moving multitude, to make a close examination of the monumental spire. At its corners stood four more beautiful groups of statuary. All around its base ran a marble frieze—a procession of life-size figures of all the mighty poets, painters, architects the ages have given to the world—Homer, Virgil, Dante, Michael Angelo, Raphael—all the world's supremely gifted men. Under the rich vault stood a massy pedestal, and through the gilded arches the sunlight streamed upon it. We moved away again, and stood outside the railing to feast again upon the general view.

I said to my comrade, "Tell me what it is."

"It is a monument—a memorial."

"Yes, I see—but to whom?"

"Guess."

"Guess—anyone can guess it. There is only one name worthy of it—only just one. And I pay the humble homage of a stranger, and offer his gratitude, to the nation that so honors her great son, the world's great teacher—it is Shakespeare! Glory to old England!"

"Bah! What an innocent you are! It is Prince Albert!"

It was too true. Napoleon's tomb at Paris has long ranked as the most sumptuous testimonial to departed greatness that Europe could show—but it is insignificant compared to this memorial which England has erected to keep green in the affectionate admiration of future generations a most excellent foreign gentleman who was a happy type of the Good, and the Kind, the Well-Meaning, the Mediocre, the Commonplace— and who did no more for his country than five hundred trades- men did in his own time, whose works are forgotten. The finest monument in the world erected to glorify—the *Commonplace*. It is the most genuinely humorous idea I have met with in this grave land. Presently the statue of the good, kind, well-meaning

gentleman will be placed upon the monumental pedestal—
and then what a satire upon human glory it will be to see
Homer and Shakespeare and Milton and Michael Angelo and
all that long marble array of the world's demigods around the
base, bracing their shoulders to the genial work and support-
ing their brother in his high seat.

I still feel some lingering discomfort that this princely structure was not built for Shakespeare—but after all, maybe he
does not need it as much as the other.

We turned about and saw a prodigious building, constructed
of cream-colored stone—and every stone in the pile curiously
and elaborately ornamented with the chisel—no end of flowers, and birds, and reptiles, all carved in painstaking detail.
The building will seat ten thousand persons, and great concerts are given there. Princes, dukes, earls, and bankers buy
boxes there for 999 years, just as they would buy a piece of real
estate, and they pay $5,000 for the said box and will transmit
it to their posterity. This palatial place is called Albert Hall,
and was erected as just one more testimonial to departed
mediocrity. Well, it is best to have a supply of memorials,
to guard against accidents. I mean to have an assortment of
tombstones myself.

We passed into the International Exhibition and found several busts and pictures of Prince Albert. Glory is a singular
thing. I find only three individuals prodigiously glorified in
monumental stone here, out of England's great long list of
immortal names—the mighty Wellington, the peerless Nel-
son, and the kindly foreign gentleman who reared a large
family of excellent children, dabbled in amateur agriculture,
law and science, distributed prizes to mechanics' societies, and
gave a notable impulse to industry by admiring it.

The inscription on the splendid monument yonder reads:

"QUEEN VICTORIA AND HER PEOPLE
TO THE MEMORY OF ALBERT, PRINCE CONSORT,
AS A TRIBUTE OF THEIR GRATITUDE
FOR A LIFE DEVOTED TO THE PUBLIC GOOD."

It is the oddest reversing of obligations that one can imagine.
England found Albert very obscure and rather stinted in
worldly goods for one in his social position. She gave him
wealth, married him to a young and beautiful queen and paid
him homage all his life as the second personage in the greatest

empire of this age. These were not trifles. There must be a mistake somewhere. Doubtless the Prince designed this monument himself, and intended to put on it this inscription:

"PRINCE ALBERT TO THE QUEEN AND HER PEOPLE,
AS A TRIBUTE OF HIS GRATITUDE FOR
INCALCULABLE BENEFITS CONFERRED UPON HIM."

II OLD SAINT PAUL'S

Who can look upon this venerable edifice, with its clustering memories and old traditions, without emotion! Who can contemplate its scarred and blackened walls without drifting insensibly into dreams of the historic past! Who can hold to be trivial even the least detail or appurtenance of this stately national altar! It is with diffidence that I approach the work of description, it is with humility that I offer the thoughts that crowd upon me.

Upon arriving at Saint Paul's, the first thing that bursts upon the beholder is the back yard. This fine work of art is forty-three feet long by thirty-four and a half feet wide—and all enclosed with real iron railings. The pavement is of fine oolite, or skylight, or some other stone of that geologic period, and is laid almost flat on the ground, in places. The stones are exactly square, and it is thought that they were made so by design; though of course, as in all matters of antiquarian science there are wide differences of opinion about this. The architect of the pavement was Morgan Jones, of No. 4 Piccadilly, Cheapside, Islington. He died in the reign of Richard III, of the prevailing disorder. An ax fell on his neck. The coloring of the pavement is very beautiful, and will immediately attract the notice of the visitor. Part of it is white and the other part black. The part that is white has been washed. This was done upon the occasion of the coronation of George II, and the person who did it was knighted, as the reader will already have opined. The iron railings cannot be too much admired. They were designed and constructed by Ralph Benson, of No. 9 Grace Church Street, Fen Church Street, Upper Terrace, Tottenham Court Road, Felter Lane, London, C. E., by special appointment blacksmith to His Royal Majesty, George III, of gracious memory, and were done at his own shop, by his own hands, and under his own personal supervision. Relics of this great artist's inspiration are exceedingly rare, and are valued at enormous sums; however, two shovels and a horseshoe made by him are on file at the British Museum, and no stranger should go away from London without seeing them. One of the shovels is undoubtedly genuine, but all authorities agree that the other one is spurious. It is not known which is the spurious one, and this is unfortunate, for nothing connected with this great man can be deemed of trifling importance. It is said that he was buried at Westminster Abbey, but was taken up and hanged in chains at Tyburn at the time of the Restoration, under the impression that he was Cromwell. But this is considered doubtful, by some, because he was not yet born at the time of the Restoration. The railings are nine feet three inches high, from the top of the stone pediment to the spearheads that form the apex, and twelve feet four inches high from the ground to the apex, the stone pediment being three feet one inch high, all of solid stone. The railings are not merely stood up on the pediment, but are mortised in, in the most ravishing manner. It was originally intended to make the railings two inches higher than they are, but the idea was finally abandoned, for some reason or other. This is greatly to be regretted, because it makes the fence out of proportion to the rest of Saint Paul's, and seriously mars the general effect. The spearheads upon the tops of the railings were gilded upon the death of Henry VIII, out of respect for the memory of that truly great King. The artist who performed the work was knighted by the regency, and hanged by Queen Mary when she came into power. No charge is made for contemplating the railings, or looking through them or climbing over them—which is in marked and generous contrast to some of the other sights of London. All you have to do is to apply to a member of the Common Council and get a letter to the Lord Mayor, who will give you a note to the Lord High Chamberlain of the Exchequer, who will grant you a pass, good for two days, together with a return ticket. This is much simpler than the system observed by the custodians of some of the other sights of London. You can walk, but it is best to go in a cab, for there is no place in London which is less than two miles and a half from any other place. I am not speaking heedlessly, but from experience. At all the other public buildings and parks in London, there is an arched and prodigious gateway which is special and sacred to the Queen, who is either sixty feet high or the gateways don't fit—but at Saint Paul's the case is different.

There is no special gate for the Queen, and so I do not know how she gets in there. It must be very inconvenient to go through a common highway when one is not used to it.

The stone pediment upon which the iron railings stand was designed and erected by William Marlow, of 14 Threadneedle Street, Paternoster Row, St. Giles's, Belgravia, W. C., and is composed of alternate layers of rock, one above the other, and all cemented together in the most compact and impressive manner. The style of its architecture is a combination of the Pre-Raphaelite and the Renaissance—just enough of the Pre-Raphaelite to make it firm and substantial, and just enough of the Renaissance to impart to the whole a calm and gracious expression. There is nothing like this stone wall in England. We have no such artists nowadays. To find true art, we must go back to the past. Let the visitor note the tone of this wall, and the feeling. No work of art can be intelligently and enjoyably contemplated unless you know about tone and feeling; unless you know all about tone and feeling, and can tell at a glance which is the tone and which is the feeling—and can talk about it with the guidebook shut up. I will venture to say that there is more tone in that stone wall than was ever hurled into a stone wall before; and as for feeling, it is just suffocated with it. As a whole, this fence is absolutely without its equal. If Michael Angelo could have seen this fence, would he have wasted his years sitting on a stone worshiping the cathedral of Florence? No; he would have spent his life gazing at this fence, and he would have taken a wax impression of it with him when he died. Michael Angelo and I may be considered extravagant, but as for me, if you simply mention art, I cannot be calm. I can go down on my knees before one of those decayed and venerable old masters that you have to put a sign on to tell which side of it you are looking at, and I do not want any bread, I do not want any meat, I do not want any air to breathe—I can *live*, in the tone and the feeling of it. Expression—expression is the thing—in art. I do not care what it expresses, and I cannot most always sometimes tell, generally, but expression is what I worship, it is what I glory in, with all my impetuous nature. All the traveling world are just like me.

Marlow, the architect and builder of the stone pediment I was speaking of, was the favorite pupil of the lamented Hugh Miller, and worked in the same quarry with him. Specimens of the stone, for the cabinet, can be easily chipped off by the tourist with his hammer, in the customary way. I will observe that the stone was brought from a quarry on the Surrey side, near London. You can go either by Blackfriars Bridge, or Westminster Bridge or the Thames tunnel—fare, two shillings in a cab. It is best seen at sunrise, though many prefer moonlight.

The front yard of Saint Paul's is just like the back yard, except that it is adorned with a very noble and imposing statue of a black woman which is said to have resembled Queen Anne, in some respects. It is five feet four inches high from the top of the figure to the pedestal, and nine feet seven inches from the top of the figure to the ground, the pedestal being four feet three inches high—all of solid stone. The figure measures eleven inches around the arm, and fifty-three inches around the body. The rigidity of the drapery has been much admired.

I will not make any description of the rest of Old Saint Paul's, for that has already been done in every book upon London that has thus far been written, and therefore the reader must be measurably familiar with it. My only object is to instruct the reader upon matters which have been strangely neglected by other tourists, and if I have supplied a vacuum which must often have been painfully felt, my reward is sufficient. I have endeavored to furnish the exact dimensions of everything in feet and inches, in the customary exciting way, and likewise to supply names and dates and gushings upon art which will instruct the future tourist how to feel and what to think, and how to tell it when he gets home.

III   THE BRITISH MUSEUM

Saturdays the great reading room of the British Museum is full of preachers stealing sermons for next day! So said Mr. Woodward, chief of the geological department. We were looking down from a gallery upon the busy scene—it *looked* busy, for there were one or two people scribbling and referring at every table, almost. But Mr. W. said, "You ought to see it *Saturdays!*" They not only copy sermons, but tear them bodily out of the books. And Vandals of other kinds tear leaves out of valuable books for other purposes, although the Museum furnishes every possible convenience for its visitors.

As usual, Mr. Lee* took me to headquarters and told the
Museum people who I was, and straightway they treated me
with every kindness and courtesy—and straightway, also, Mr.
Woodward took us into the gold room—one of those jealously
guarded places which one must usually go through some red
tape to get into. Lee went to his business and Mr. W. showed
me through some eighteen miles of tall bookcases—a labyrinth
of circles and galleries. We have put off the rest of the library
for the present.

But I (upon recommendation of two householders of London) am provided with a ticket to the Reading Room, and
this is always open, whereas the rest of the Museum is only
open three days in the week.

What a place it is!

Mention some very rare curiosity of a peculiar nature—a
something which you have read about somewhere but never
seen—they show you a dozen! They show you all the possible
varieties of that thing! They show you curiously wrought and
jeweled necklaces of beaten gold worn by the Ancient Egyptians, Assyrians, Etruscans, Greeks, Britons—every people, of
the forgotten ages, indeed. They show you the ornaments of
all the tribes and peoples that live or ever did live. Then they
show you a cast taken from Cromwell's face in death; then the
venerable vase that once contained the ashes of Xerxes; then
you drift into some other room and stumble upon a world of
the flint hatchets of prehistoric days; and reindeer horn
handles; and pieces of bone with figures of animals delicately
carved upon them; and long rows of bone fishhooks and needles
of the period—everything, indeed, connected with the household economy of the cave and lake dwellers—and every object
too, so repeated, and multiplied, and remultiplied that they
suddenly whisk away your doubts and you find yourself accept-
ing as a fact that these implements and ornaments are not
scattered accidents, but deliberately designed and tediously
wrought, and in very common use in some queer age of the
world or other. And the fact that many of them are found in
ruined habitations in the bottoms of Swiss lakes, and many
in caverns in other parts of Europe (buried under slowly
created and very thick layers of limestone), does not encourage one to try to claim these parties as very recent kin.
And then you pass along and perhaps you ask if they have got

* A businessman, "fellow in several royal societies," who had befriended Clemens. [B. DV.]

such a thing as a mummy about their clothes—and bless your heart and they rush you into a whole Greenwood Cemetery of them—old mummies, young mummies, he mummies, she mummies, high-toned mummies, ragged mummies, old slouches, mummies in good whole coffins, mummies on the half-shell, mummies with money, mummies that are "busted," kings and emperors, loafers and bummers, all straightened out as comfortable and happy in a Christian museum as if they had brought their knitting with them and this was the very hotel they had been hunting for, for four thousand years and upwards. And while you are wondering if these defunct had human feelings, human sympathies, human emotions like your own, you turn pensively about and find an eloquent answer: an Egyptian woman's enormous chignon and the box she carried it in when she went out to a party! You want to kiss that poor old half-bushel of curled and plaited hair; you want to uncover the glass case and shed some tears on it. You recognize the fact that in the old, old times, woman was the same quaint, fascinating, eccentric muggins she is in these.

They were strange, strange people in those old forgotten times. But I wonder how the mummies walked, with all those bandages on.

I am wonderfully thankful for the British Museum. Nobody comes bothering around me—nobody elbows me—all the room and all the light I want under this huge dome—no disturbing noises—and people standing ready to bring me a copy of pretty much any book that ever was printed under the sun—and if I choose to go wandering about the long corridors and galleries of the great building, the secrets of all the earth and all the age are laid open to me. I am not capable of expressing my gratitude for the British Museum—it seems as if I do not know any but little words and weak ones.

From the Manuscript of "A Tramp Abroad" (1879): The French and the Comanches

NOW as to cruelty, savagery, and the spirit of massacre. These do not add a grace to the world's partly civilized races, yet at the same time they can hardly be called defects. They grow naturally out of the social system; the system could not be perfect without them. It is hard to draw a line here, with any great degree of exactness, between the French, the Comanches, and the several other nations existing upon the same moral and social level. It must in candor be admitted that in one point the Comanches rank higher than the French, in that they do not fight among themselves, whereas a favorite pastime with the French, from time immemorial, has been the burning and slaughtering of each other. No weapon has drunk such rivers of French blood as the French sword. No hatred has been so implacable as the Frenchman's hatred of his brother. No other creature's religion has wrought such marvels of murderous atrocity as the meek and lowly religion of the Frenchman. However, the last sentence is in a sense unfair, in the present comparison, since the Comanche has had no religion, and hence no pressing motive to reform his brother by killing him.

The Turks have fought among themselves, sometimes, so have many others among the inferior nations, but in truth civil war has never reached the entire perfection of bitterness, effectiveness, and immortal activity and perseverance in any but two communal organizations, those of the French and of the Kilkenny cats.

I very much doubt if the French are more cruel than the Comanches; I think they are only more ingenious in their methods. If this can be established as a fact, it will be evidence that the Frenchman is a higher being than the Comanche.

The French nobility invented several striking and remarkable customs, and preserved them, through the intelligent docility of the people, for a thousand years. One was the right, after renting a farm to a man, to ride down the man's crops, in chase after game, without having to pay for the destruction caused. Another right was to forbid the man to enclose his farm with walls or fences to keep out predatory wild animals—for fences obstructed the chase. Another was the lord's right to keep a dovecote, and not have to pay for the crops which the doves ate up, yet be free to punish any victim who killed one of the creatures. Another was the lord's right to keep an oven and a mill, and compel the commoner to take his baking and grinding there, and pay double price. Another was the lord's right to seize the lands and goods of widows and orphans when the head of the family died intestate. Another was the lord's right to take about a fifth part of the sale-money when lands within his jurisdiction changed hands. But these are minor cruelties— any partly civilized community could invent them and endure them. Higher in the scale are these others—namely, the lord's right to make the peasants, after working all day, sit up and whip the ponds all night with boughs, to prevent the frogs' music from disturbing my lord's slumbers; the lord's right to cut open a peasant and warm his feet in him, as in a foot muff, when the chase had wearied my lord and made him cold; and, finally, comes le droit du seigneur—let it go in French, it would soil the English language to describe it in that tongue. The Comanches might beat these last three rights, possibly, but they could not beat them much. However, French ingenuity struck its supremest altitude during the Revolution, when the revolutionists tied naked men to naked women, and threw them into the river. This was a step beyond the invention of the Comanche. Therefore here the Comanche fails and the Frenchman takes the precedence. As this thing occurred less than a hundred years ago, we are able to believe that the Frenchman has not yet lost his inventive art, nor possibly the disposition to exercise it.

In one thing the French stand almost alone. The spirit of massacre seems to be theirs by divine right. No other nation has had it so conspicuously. The French have almost monopol- ized it during ages. Long before St. Bartholomew's, they had learned to know and love the deep pleasures of the massacre. St. Bartholomew's is so monumental that its vast shadow hides the noble array of massacres that lie behind it; we see them so dimly that we scarcely note them—but they are there, just the same. If certain of the greater ones had been done in England, they would blacken the sun of her history like an eclipse; but being done in the native home of massacre, they seem as natural and proper as the splotches on a leper, and provoke as little attention.

St. Bartholomew's was unquestionably the finest thing of the kind ever devised and accomplished in the world. All the best people took a hand in it, the King and the Queen Mother included. The time was 1572. There was a misunderstanding on a religious point. The Frenchman is nothing if not pious. He is not content to be pious all by himself, he requires his neighbor to be pious also—otherwise he will kill him and make him so. Yes, if that neighbor declines to lead a holy life, he will take an ax and convert him. The Frenchman is a social being, and does not wish to occupy heaven in solitude—therefore he provides company for himself. At the time I speak of, it was not merely one neighbor who had gone astray as to religion, but a full half of the nation. This was a bad business. The Catholic chiefs were grieved to see this sorrowful sinfulness, and took counsel concerning the best way to cure it. The Queen Mother, whose wisdom and holiness were perfect, suggested the usual national remedy, a massacre. The idea was approved and the massacre was ordered, just as other people would order a breakfast. The midnight between two August days was appointed for the beginning of the good work, and notice was sent out to the various towns and cities. The truly pious prepared their arms, preserved their secret, and waited; they visited and were visited by their sinful and unsuspecting neighbors as usual, and the doom that was in the air gave no token. The King held the kindliest communion with the leader of the sinners; and if this latter had been of an observant turn he could have seen there the very gun with which his majesty was going to cripple him from the palace windows a little later.

The appointed hour came, and the midnight tocsin burst upon the stillness with its clangor. The pious were ready, the sinful were taken by surprise. Houses were invaded, men and women were slaughtered in their chambers or on their stairs, children were brained against the walls. The devout work was kept up two days and three nights, the river was clogged with the bodies of the slain, the streets were piled with corpses, the air was foul with the decaying flesh of men who were martyrs to their own slowness of invention—for they were Frenchmen, and if they had happened to think of the idea first, they would have massacred the others. Seventy thousand lives were taken in those two or three days in France, and the true religion retired from its exploit so much strengthened that the other side was never able to seriously threaten its supremacy afterward.

There have been French massacres since, of course. The Reign of Terror was one protracted and enjoyable one, and we have had some in our time, notably that of the 2nd December and several under the Commune toward the close of the Franco-Prussian War. But none of these are half such matters of pride to the French as their peerless St. Bartholomew's.

The most attractive feature of the French national character, and its most encouraging one to the missionary, is its admirable and unapproachable docility. We look upon rabbits as being meek. But what is the meekness of the rabbit to the meekness of the Frenchman? Are there any rabbits that would allow themselves to be abused, insulted and trodden under foot persistently and continuously for a thousand years and never offer to bite? Europe is freckled all over with daring little communities which have risen against powerful oppressors time and time again, and compelled redress. The list stretches out to weariness. William Tells and Wat Tylers have been common nearly everywhere but in France. Yet even France rose at last—and would have retired to its warren again quite contented with a cuff and a bonbon if the foolish King had offered them, but it was not his style to do the needful thing at the needful time, so the chance went by. Then the nation cast its rabbit skin and put on its other national garment, the tiger skin; being closely pressed by Europe in arms, it went a step further and asserted its manhood, and was doubtless surprised to find how much it had of it. Napoleon, the great foreigner, brought the people's soldiership up to the last summit of perfection; and when he got ready he dressed the nation in their rabbit skins again and put his foot on their necks, and they glorified him for it. Napoleon III accommodated them in the same way, to their vast satisfaction.

The foreigner has been a great boon to France. France's great men have been rather usually foreign-born—the present time is not an exception to the rule—and these wise persons seem to have well understood how to please the average citizen. The average citizen requires "glory"—that is the main thing; plenty of glory, plenty of noise, plenty of show, plenty of equality and fraternity, plenty of masked balls and fantastic nonsense, plenty of gammon and brag; plenty of assurances that the world's eye is upon him, that his wife sets the fashion in clothes and he in skin-deep politeness; plenty of reminders that his tongue is the court language of the nations and that Paris is the sun and could robe the earth in intellectual darkness by going out; plenty of *Vive la République* today, *Vive le Roi* tomorrow, *Vive la Commune* next day and *Vive the devil* the day after; plenty of high-sounding painless duels to cock up his stricken honor again; plenty of piousness and indecency and massacre and hurrah—these he requires in life, and a rattling funeral to end up with, with a priest and a lantern in the lead, an imitation major general on the hearse box, and a string of vacant mourning coaches tagging after—then he is satisfied, and sails rejoicing up among the other angels to tell about it. These grandeurs are inexpensive, and the great foreigners who have ruled France have found their profit in furnishing them.

As I have said, the Frenchman's docility is the most beautiful trait in the national character, and will presently become his most useful endowment; for by it our missionaries will uplift him as one lifts a rabbit by the ears. The Frenchman is made up of the littlest littlenesses conceivable, and the greatest greatnesses.* The tiger that is in him—the stealthy, blood-loving, massacring instinct—fits him to become, through repression and careful training, the mightiest of soldiers. The rabbit-docility which has been bred in him by ages of meek putting-up with wrongs and indignities is the thing which will enable him to endure this repression and training without a

---

* When d'Aiguillon sent his midnight commands to the refractory Parliament of Paris to resume duty, 160 out of the 200 members sat up in their beds and boldly and bravely refused. Each individual did this heroism by himself and out of his own native greatness, for he could not *know* that the others, or any of them, would be steadfast and do the like. By contrast with this, observe the pettiness which moves each new governmental system in France to wipe out every historical reminder of the system which preceded it, even to the names of streets. Napoleon put his statue on the Vendôme column; the succeeding systems replaced that statue with something else; when the Commune came into power, it pulled down column and all; now the Republic has re-erected the column and surmounted it with a stone figure representing the Genius of something or other, I don't know exactly what—French fickleness, perhaps. [M. T.]

murmur. His gigantic vanity will move him to attempt miracles in art, mechanics, statesmanship, and literature which would appall another, and his fervid and frantic imagination and his restless energy and diligence will enable him to carry them to a successful conclusion.

Now if my work has been intelligibly done, I have shown that the Frenchman is in some respects the superior of the Chinaman, in others the equal of the Turk and the Dahomian, and in hardly any particular the conspicuous inferior of the Comanche. I hoped and believed I could do this; I think I have succeeded. There is little question, in my mind, that France is entitled to a distinguished place among the partly civilized peoples of our globe.

I have the highest hopes of France, I have the deepest and most heartfelt yearnings for her moral and intellectual elevation and enlightenment. But I know and feel that this great benefit cannot come to her, in perfection, through the restricted and unsystematized efforts of our American colony, active and holy and precious as these are—no, there is but one way, the employment of a trained corps of lay American missionaries, armed with official rank for their protection, furnished with the ribbon of the legion of honor to render them inconspicuous and avert notice and jealousy, and paid by the government out of appropriations created by a special tax. Let us all aid in helping the Frenchman. Let us take to our hearts this disparaged and depreciated link between man and the simian and raise him up to brotherhood with us.

From an Unfinished Burlesque of Books on Etiquette

I   AT THE FUNERAL

DO NOT criticize the person in whose honor the entertainment is given.

Make no remarks about his equipment. If the handles are plated, it is best to seem to not observe it.

If the odor of the flowers is too oppressive for your comfort, remember that they were not brought there for you, and that the person for whom they were brought suffers no inconvenience from their presence.

Listen, with as intense an expression of attention as you can command, to the official statement of the character and history of the person in whose honor the entertainment is given; and if these statistics should seem to fail to tally with the facts, in places, do not nudge your neighbor, or press your foot upon his toes, or manifest, by any other sign, your awareness that taffy is being distributed.

If the official hopes expressed concerning the person in whose honor the entertainment is given are known by you to be oversized, let it pass—do not interrupt.

At the moving passages, be moved—but only according to the degree of your intimacy with the parties giving the entertainment, or with the party in whose honor the entertainment is given. Where a blood relation sobs, an intimate friend should choke up, a distant acquaintance should sigh, a stranger should merely fumble sympathetically with his handkerchief. Where the occasion is military, the emotions should be graded according to military rank, the highest officer present taking precedence in emotional violence, and the rest modifying their feelings according to their position in the service.

Do not bring your dog.

II AT A FIRE

*Form of Tender of Rescue from Strange Young Gentleman to Strange
Young Lady at a Fire.*

Although through the fiat of a cruel fate, I have been debarred the
gracious privilege of your acquaintance, permit me, Miss [here insert
name, if known], the inestimable honor of offering you the aid of a
true and loyal arm against the fiery doom which now o'ershadows you
with its crimson wing. [This form to be memorized, and practiced in
private.]

Should she accept, the young gentleman should offer his arm—
bowing, and observing "Permit me"—and so escort her to the
fire escape and deposit her in it (being extremely careful, if
she have no clothes on but her night dress, not to seem to
notice the irregularity). No form of leavetaking is permissible,
further than a formal bow, accompanied by a barely perceptible
smile of deferential gratitude for the favor which the young
lady has accorded—this smile to be completed at the moment
the fire escape starts to slide down, then the features to be
recomposed instantly.

A compulsory introduction at a fire is not binding upon the
young lady. The young gentleman cannot require recognition
at her hands when he next meets her, but must leave her
unembarrassed to decide for herself whether she will continue
the acquaintanceship or ignore it.

To return to the fire. If the boarding house is not provided
with a fire escape, the young gentleman will use such other
means of rescue as circumstances shall afford. But he will not
need to change the form of his proffer of assistance; for this
speech has been purposely framed in such a way as to apply
with equal felicity to all methods of rescue from fire. If egress
may be had to the street by the stairway, the young gentleman
will offer his arm and escort the young lady down; if retreat
in that direction is cut off by the fire, he will escort her to the
floor above and lower her to the street by a rope, fastening it
by slip-noose under her armpits, with the knot behind (at the
same time bowing and saying "Permit me"); or if no rope
be procurable, he will drop her from the balcony upon soft
substances to be provided by the populace below—always observing "Permit me," and accompanying the remark with a

slight inclination of the head. In either ascending or descending the stairs, the young gentleman shall walk beside the young lady, if the stairs are wide enough to allow it; otherwise he must precede her. In no case must he follow her. This is *de rigueur.*

MEM. In rescuing a chambermaid, presentation of card is not necessary, neither should one say "Permit me." The form of tender service should also be changed. Example:

Form of Tender of Rescue from Young Gentleman to Chambermaid at a Fire.

There is no occasion for alarm, Mary [insertion of surname not permissible]; keep cool, do everything just as I tell you, and, *D.V.,* I will save you.

Anything more elaborate than this, as to diction and sentiment, would be in exceedingly bad taste, in the case of a chambermaid. Yet at the same time, brusqueries are to be avoided. Such expressions as "Ccme, git!" should never fall from the lips of a true gentleman at a fire. No, not even when addressed to the humblest domestic. Brevity is well; but even brevity cannot justify vulgarity.

In assisting at a fire in a boarding house, the true gentleman will always save the young ladies first—making no distinction in favor of personal attractions, or social eminence, or pecuniary predominance—but taking them as they come, and firing them out with as much celerity as shall be consistent with decorum. There are exceptions, of course, to all rules; the exceptions to this one are:

Partiality, in the matter of rescue, to be shown to:

1. Fiancées.
2. Persons toward whom the operator feels a tender sentiment, but has not yet declared himself.
3. Sisters.
4. Stepsisters.
5. Nieces.
6. First cousins.
7. Cripples.
8. Second cousins.
9. Invalids.
10. Young-lady relations by marriage.
11. Third cousins, and young-lady friends of the family.
12. The Unclassified.

Parties belonging to these twelve divisions should be saved in the order in which they are named.

The operator must keep himself utterly calm, and his line of procedure constantly in mind; otherwise the confusion around him will be almost sure to betray him into very embarrassing breaches of etiquette. Where there is much smoke, it is often quite difficult to distinguish between new Relatives by Marriage and Unclassified young ladies; wherefore it is provided that if the operator, in cases of this sort, shall rescue a No. 12 when he should have rescued a No. 10, it is not requisite that he carry No. 12 back again, but that he leave her where she is without remark, and go and fetch out No. 10. An apology to No. 10 is not imperative; still, it is good form to offer it. It may be deferred, however, one day—but no longer. [In a case of this nature which occurred during the first day of the Chicago fire, where the operator saved a No. 7 when a No. 6 was present but overlooked in the smoke, it was held by competent authorities, that the postponement of the apology for the extraordinary term of three days was justified, it being considered that the one-day term during which the apology must be offered means the day after the fire, and therefore does not begin until the fire is out. This decision was sustained by the several Illinois courts through which it was carried; and experts are confident that it will also be sustained, eventually, in the Supreme Court of the United States—where it still lingers.]

To return to the fire.

Observe: 1's, 3's, 4's, and 5's may be carried out of the burning house, in the operator's arms—permission being first asked, and granted; 7's and 9's may be carried out without the formality of asking permission; the other grades may not be carried out, except they themselves take the initiative, and signify, by word or manner, their desire to partake of this attention.

Form for Requesting Permission to Carry a No. 1, 3, 4, or 5, out of a Boarding House Which Is on Fire.

The bonds of [here insert "tenderness," in the case of No. 1; or "blood," in the other cases] which enfold us in their silken tie, warrant me, my dear [here insert given name, in all cases; and without prefix], in offering to you the refuge of my arms in fleeing the fiery doom which now, with crimson wing, o'ershadows us.

In cases where a member of one of the prohibited grades signifies a desire to be carried out of the fire, response should be made in the following form—accompanied by a peculiarly profound obeisance:

Form of Response to Indication on the part of a 2, 6, 8, 10, 11 or 12 that she Desires to be Carried Out of a Fire in Arms of Young Gentleman.

In view of the circumstance, Madmoselle [insert *name* only in cases where the party is a 6 or an 8—be careful about this], that but fragile and conventional [here—in case of a No. 2—insert "Alas!"] are the bonds which enfold us in their silken tie, it is with deepest sense of the signal distinction which your condescension has conferred upon me, that I convey to you the refuge of my arms in fleeing the fiery doom which now, with crimson wing, o'ershadows us.

Other material in boarding house is to be rescued in the following order:

13. Babies.
14. Children under 10 years of age.
15. Young widows.
16. Young married females.
17. Elderly married ditto.
18. Elderly widows.
19. Clergymen.
20. Boarders in general.
21. Female domestics.
22. Male ditto.
23. Landlady.
24. Landlord.
25. Firemen.
26. Furniture.
27. Mothers-in-law.

Arbitrary introductions, made under fire, to 12's through the necessity of carrying them out of the conflagration, are not binding. It rests with the young lady to renew the acquaintanceship or let it drop. If she shall desire the renewal, she may so signify by postal card; by intimation conveyed through friend of family; or by simple recognition of operator, by smile and slight inclination of head, the first time she meets him after the fire. In the resulting conversation the young gentleman must strictly refrain from introducing the subject of fire,

or indeed of combustibles of any kind, lest he may seem to
conceive and remember that he has lately done a heroic action,
or at least an action meriting complimentary acknowledgment;
whereas, on the contrary, he should studiedly seem to have
forgotten the circumstance, until the young lady shall herself
—if she so please—refer to it; in which case he will bow repeatedly, smiling continuously, and accompanying each bow
with the observation (uttered in a soft, apparently embarrassed, yet gratified voice), "'m very glad, 'm sure, 'm very
glad, 'm sure."

Offers of marriage to parties who are being carried out from
a boarding house on fire are considered to be in questionable
taste, for the reason that the subject of the proposition is not
likely to be mistress of her best judgment at so alarming and
confusing a time, and therefore it may chance that she is taken
at a disadvantage. Indeed, the most authoritative canons of
high breeding limit such offers inflexibly to cases where the
respondent is a No. 2. In these instances, the following form
should be observed:

*Form of Offer of Marriage from Young Gentleman to a No. 2, during
Process of Extracting Her from Boarding House on Fire, and Con-
veying Her out of the Same in His Arms.*

Ah, I supplicate, I beseech, I implore thee, dearest [here insert
given name of party only], to have compassion upon thy poor kneeling henchmen [do not attempt to kneel—this is but a figure of speech]
and deign to be his! Deign to engender into bonds of tenderness
those bonds of chill conventionality which enfold us in their silken
tie, and he will ever bless the day thou didst accept the refuge of
his arms in fleeing the fiery doom which now, with crimson wing,
o'ershadows us.

Enough has been said, now, as to the conduct which a
young gentleman of culture and breeding should observe in
the case of a boarding house on fire. The same rules apply,
with but slight variations (which will suggest themselves to
the operator), to fire in a church, private house, hotel, railway
train, or on shipboard—indeed to all fires in the ordinary walks
of life.

In the case of a ship on fire, evening dress must be omitted.
The true gentleman never wears evening dress at sea, even in
case of a fire.

The speeches to be used at a fire may also, with but slight

alteration, be wielded with effect upon disastrous occasions of other sorts. For instance, in tendering rescue from destruction by hurricane, or earthquake, or runaway team, or railway collision (where no conflagration ensues), the operator should merely substitute "fatal doom" for "fiery doom"; and in cases of ordinary shipwreck or other methods of drowning, he should say "watery doom." No other alterations are necessary, for the "crimson wing" applies to all calamities of a majestic sort, and is a phrase of exceeding finish and felicity.

Observe, in conclusion: Offers of marriage, during episode of runaway team, are to be avoided. A lady is sufficiently embarrassed at such a time; any act tending to add to this embarrassment is opposed to good taste, and therefore reprehensible.

III VISITING CARDS

One of the ablest of our recent works on Deportment* has this remark:

> To the unrefined or the underbred person, the visiting-card is but a trifling and insignificant bit of paper; but to the cultured disciple of social law it conveys a subtle and unmistakable intelligence.
> Its texture, style of engraving, and even the hour of leaving it, combine to place the stranger whose name it bears in a pleasant or a disagreeable attitude, even before his manners, conversation, and face have been able to explain his social position.
> The receiver of a visitor's card makes a careful study of its style. If it is in perfect taste, she admires him unconsciously for this evidence of excellent style, refinement, and familiarity with the details of a high social position and delicate breeding.

All this is wisely conceived, and well said. For the cultured, these hints are sufficient; but some elaboration of the matter seems worth while, in the interest of the partly cultured and the ignorant. Now observe, the points noted as concerns the card—and they are exceedingly important—are as follows:

1. Its texture.
2. Style of engraving.
3. Hour of leaving it.

If these fall short of the standard established by social law, the visitor is placed in a "disagreeable attitude"; but if, after

---

* *Social Etiquette of New York:* D. Appleton & Co. [M. T.]

a careful study of card and hour, the lady finds in them the regulation evidences of the visitor's perfect taste, she "admires him unconsciously." Let us now enter, carefully and orderly, upon particulars.

As to texture. Always use linen cards—never the cheap cotton styles. This is *de rigueur.*

If you are a mere "Mr.," let your name be engraved in a delicate script; your address, in the same script, must be at the bottom of the card, in the left-hand corner; that is, if you are a bachelor; but if you are married, it must be placed in the right-hand corner.

If you bear a title, you should use a German text of a somewhat bold and pronounced character. In America (but in America only), your wife may be referred to by your title—and she may also put it on her card. Examples:

𝕸rs. 𝕾uperintendent-of-𝕻ublic-𝕴nstruction 𝕵ones

𝕿he 𝕽ocks, 𝕳ogback-on-the-𝕳udson

𝕸rs. 𝕮lerk-of-the-𝕭oard-of-𝕬ldermen 𝕳ooligan

𝕿he 𝕿ombs, 2ᵇ 𝕱loor, 𝕹ew 𝖄ork

𝕸rs. 2ᵇ-𝕷ieut.-𝕮o.-𝕭.,-42ᵇ-𝕽egt.-𝕹.-𝖄.-
𝕸ounted-𝕸ilitia 𝕭aggs

64 𝕿hompson 𝕾t., 𝕹ew 𝖄ork

𝕿hursdays

"Thursdays" means that that is her reception day—a reminder that formal calls are not received there on any other day of the week.

The *placing* of the name is a matter of moment. It should be engraved on the *back* of the court cards; and on the *front* of the spot-cards and the joker. For obvious reasons the ace of spades is an exception to this rule—the name goes on the back of it.

A single remark, here, may not be out of place: Never use a second-hand deck, when making a ceremonious call. And never use what in vulgar parlance is called an old greasy deck, except in the case of social inferiors and poor kin.

Now as to the *hour*. Never pay a morning call (of ceremony) before breakfast. Figuratively speaking, this law, like the laws of the Medes and Persians, is written in blood. To call before breakfast would in many cases subject the stranger to the suspicion of desiring to compel an invitation to that meal; and would as often subject the host to the necessity of withholding such invitation—for the reason that the European breakfast (now the only correct thing in our higher circles) bars all sudden additions, there not being enough of it for the family. Now inasmuch as the stranger cannot know everybody's breakfast hour, and therefore is liable to infringe the rule innocently, the canons of fashion have provided for him a simple and at the same time sufficient protection: when he has the slightest reason to fear that he has called too early, he must write "B.T.B." in the upper left-hand corner of his card—which signifies *Been to breakfast.*

Do not make an evening visit of ceremony after bedtime. One is liable to be shot. This is on account of the prevalence of burglars. But aside from this consideration, a visit at so late an hour would amount to a familiarity, and would therefore place the stranger in a disagreeable attitude.

Between the limits above defined, visits may be paid at any hour you may choose; though of course one must not wittingly intrude at luncheon or dinner.

Signification, etc., of the Cards
   Diamonds—Independent means, and no occupation.
   Hearts—Love.
   Clubs—Ultra fashion.
   Spades—Neutral.
In houses of the best fashion, at the present day, you will find an ornamental table in the hall, near the front door. Deposit your card upon this.

A word just here: Make no unnecessary remarks to the servant. Do not ask him How's the family; nor How's things; nor What's up—nor any such matter. It is but a transparent artifice, whose intent is to move such as are within hearing to admire how easy, and unembarrassed, and veteran to the ways of society the visitor is. All exhibitions of this sort are low. And do not shake hands with the servant, either coming or going; it is an excess of familiarity, and hence is in bad taste. If you know the servant, you may speak his Christian name, if you so desire, but you must not abbreviate it. You

may address him as Thomas or William; but never as Tom
or Tommy, or as Bill, Buck, or Billy. In the best society one
goes even further, and studiedly *miscalls* the name, substi-
tuting William for Thomas, and Thomas for William. This
is quite good form, since it gives one the appearance of not
charging his mind with things of trifling importance. When
one moves in the supremest rank of fashion, and has an as-
sured place there, it is his right, sanctioned by old custom, to
call *all* servants Thomas, impartially. When the Thomas is a
female, the designation stands for her surname.

Now as to a discriminating use of the visiting card—a very
important matter since this utensil—so to call it—is capable
of expressing quite nice shades of sentiment or purpose.

On a first visit, the person of independent means will indicate this fact by deposing a diamond on the table above referred to. If he is worth only about $200,000, he will deposit
a deuce; if he is worth more than this sum, he will indicate
it by depositing the proper card, guiding himself by the following table of values.

Denomination	Value
Trey	$ 300,000
Four	400,000
Five	500,000
Six	600,000
Seven	700,000
Eight	800,000
Nine	900,000
Ten	1,000,000
Jack	3,000,000
Queen	8,000,000
King	20,000,000
Ace	

The Ace has no limit. It means that the visitor owns a
bonanza, or a railway system, or a telegraph system, or a
Standard Oil monopoly.

Having once indicated, by your diamond lead, your financial
standing, you will not lead from that suit any more, upon
subsequent visits. In cases, later, of great enlargement of
capital, one may play another diamond to indicate it, but it
is not good form, except where the tender passion is concerned. It is permissible, then, if the tenderness has not been

mutual, but has been mainly concentered in the male; for if a suitor who has led a trey or a four of diamonds in the beginning, and the tenderness, after due assiduity, has not been mutual, he will often find that the acquired ability to play a jack, by and by, has a tendency to mutualize it. Indeed, it is held by some authorities that no unmutualness is so unmutual that is cannot be mutualized by an ace.

Since the club is the symbol of the highest heaven of fashion and style, it necessarily stands at the top of the deck. By virtue of this precedence the club is always trump. It not only holds over the other suits, but one may play it whenever he chooses. Remember these things. And also this: one should not lead a club, except upon the occasion of a first visit. It is necessary then—for these reasons: it indicates that the visitor is of high fashion; and it also indicates, by the denomination of the card, how high up, or how low down, in the fashionable system he belongs. If you are of new date in high circles, and not conspicuous, lead a small spot-card; if new but conspicuous, play a five or a seven, or along there somewhere; if you are of a fine old fashionable family, and personally distinguished, lead a high spot-card gauged to the size of the circumstances; if you are not distinguished, but had a distinguished grandfather, lead the jack; for distinguished great-great-great grandfather, lead the queen; for distinguished ancestor ("ancestor" means foreign and away back) propagated by titled personage, lead the king; for ancestor derived from Lady Portsmouth or other friend of royalty, lead the ace. If your sister, or other lady relative, has elevated you to connection with nobility by marrying a foreign person of title, this is the grandest of all distinctions, and takes easy precedence of each and every other claim in our upper society, and gives you right and privilege to lead the "Joker." N.B.—Since clubs are trumps always, it follows that the "Joker" always stands for a club.

The spade being neutral and noncommittal, we always use that suit when our visit is not one of a deep or peculiar significance. Hence we play the spade very much oftener than any other card. Naturally, therefore, it is called our long suit.

Now we come to the hearts. Of course this is a most important card, since its peculiar province is to lead us along the primrose path whose sweet goal is matrimony.

In opening the delicate game of love, you should lead a low card—your lowest, indeed—the deuce. How exquisitely this expresses a budding affection! You should say but little, on this first love-visit; on the contrary you should appear pensive and distraught, and seem to suffer. Do not forget to seem to suffer—this is important. Observe the effect of your card upon the lady. If she blushes, though ever so faintly, it is an elegant sign.

Be wary, be watchful, upon subsequent visits. Confine yourself strictly to the deuce; venture no farther while things seem to go well and pleasure mantles in her eye upon reception of card. Meanwhile, continue to seem to suffer, as before. But the moment you detect indifference in her face, the time has come for you to change your lead. Keep your own counsel; but the next time you come, play a low spade—an ultra neutral card. You will discover in a moment whether the lady's indifference was assumed or real. If the former, she will blench a little, and perhaps falter in her greeting. [Follow up this advantage; use first opportunity to press hand; if pressure returned, sigh; if sigh returned, appear transfigured; if cannot appear transfigured, approximate it. If pressure not returned, sigh anyhow, as above; take opportunity to speak of shortness of life—brevity of existence is better; refer to morning of life overshadowed, cold world, blighted young hopes, etc., and do the early grave business and "soon be at rest," and that sort of thing. Note effect. If evidently touched, lay into this line pretty strong; keep right along, spread it on thick. Introduce topic of sick mother (sick mother admirable material); get her to sympathize. Work in other sick relatives, as opportunity offers—but not too many; better leave three out than have one left over. Keep sharp lookout, and at right time, draw on your dead. Early dead most pathetic, perhaps, and therefore preferable. But be careful; do not overdo this feature; the first sample that palls on her, close the cemetery, and shade off onto suicide. Mem.—Leave her in tears, if it takes till breakfast.]

Next time you come, play the trey of hearts. Play it confidently—there is no occasion for fear.

You are fairly launched now, on the sweet voyage, and with a fair wind. But be ever wary; do not go too fast. Do not lead your four spot till you are sure you have gotten far enough along to warrant it. By and by, venture your five—and so on. If ever you discover that you have added a spot too soon, show instant repentance and deep humility by receding a spot or two—set yourself back a whole month, even—it will have a good effect.

Meantime, keep always prepared for rivals. For instance, if you are at the five-spot stage, and you perceive that a rival has deposited the six on the hall table, don't hesitate—play the seven and take it. Your boldness will please the lady and win your forgiveness. If your rival's heart is the biggest one in the deck, trump it—never weaken. From time to time, cases of doubt will turn up, but let them not confuse you, for there is one general law which covers these emergencies: When you are in doubt, take the trick.

By and by—let us suppose—you have at last climbed through all the stages, and the blissful moment has come for the playing your last and highest heart. You should agree upon a day and hour, with the lady, beforehand, because proposal of marriage must follow immediately upon this final play.

Let us consider that everything has been done and that the proposal is the next thing on the docket. Always propose in evening dress, if you are a civilian; in uniform, if you are in the army or navy—with sword or saber, but without revolver or spurs. The Masonic or Odd Fellows' regalia should be super-added, in both cases, if you hold the privilege. [The lady should wear orange buds which are still green and have not begun to open. And other clothing, of course.]

You should make your proposal kneeling upon one knee—using hassock or handkerchief.

Form of Proposal to Spinster—and Responses.

HE: Oh, dearest [insert given name only], will thou join thy sweet destiny to mine, and, hand in hand, journey with me adown life's tranquil stream, sharing its storms and calms, its labor and pain, its joy and sorrow, its poverty and wealth, its sickness and health, its beauteous paths, its arid wastes, and all that the inscrutable hand of fate shall pour out upon us, of sweet and bitter, till death do us part? [Weep, here.]

SHE: Oh, darling [insert given name, if handsome one—otherwise say *Reginald*], truly will thy [insert own given name] journey with thee, hand in hand, adown life's tranquil stream, sharing its storms and calms, its labor and pain, its joy and sorrow, its poverty and wealth, its sickness and health, its beauteous paths, its arid wastes, and all that the inscrutable hand of fate shall pour upon us, of sweet and bitter, till death do us part. [Weep, here.]

HE: Oh, mine own!

SHE: Ah, mine own! [Rise and embrace—but carefully, being regardful of her toilet.]

In case of a widow, proposer will use same form, merely inserting word or two of kindly reference to deceased. Widow will use same form, merely acknowledging kindly notice of deceased with sob, if affliction recent; simple sigh, if more remote.

If proposer is defeated, he may throw up his hand or call a new deal, just as he shall prefer, or as circumstances may dictate.

But if he is elected, he must now drop into the beautiful French custom of fetching a bouquet every day. His first bouquet must be entirely white; after that, a faint shade of color (red) must be added daily. Let the tint deepen gradually day by day, and with such careful precision that there shall still remain a perceptible trace of white down to the very day before the wedding. On that day the last bouquet is delivered —and it must be absolutely red—no suggestion of other color in it anywhere.

It is an admirable custom, because it is stylish, and troublesome, and instinct with delicate sentiment, if one ignores the significance which the French people attach to it. But it is going out—at least in some sections of America. In some of our best circles a new custom has already taken its place—and yet it is substantially the French one in a new guise. It is as follows. As a starter, the bridegroom-elect fetches a handkerchief; then a napkin; then a towel—and so on, gradually enlarging, by degrees; and the day before the wedding he winds up with a blanket. The sentiment is the same, and the things keep better.

We do not need to say anything about marriage settlements. Among the French and Comanches, where a bride is a mere thing of barter, worth so much cash, or so many yellow dogs or wildcat skins, the marriage settlement is necessarily a very important matter; but this is not the case with us, so we will not discuss the subject.

The Damned Human Race

I WAS THE WORLD MADE FOR MAN?

Alfred Russell Wallace's revival of the theory that this earth is at the centre of the stellar universe, and is the only habitable globe, has aroused great interest in the world.—LITERARY DIGEST

For ourselves we do thoroughly believe that man, as he lives just here on this tiny earth, is in essence and possibilities the most sublime existence in all the range of non-divine being—the chief love and delight of God.—Chicago INTERIOR (Presb.)

I SEEM to be the only scientist and theologian still remaining to be heard from on this important matter of whether the world was made for man or not. I feel that it is time for me to speak.

I stand almost with the others. They believe the world was made for man, I believe it likely that it was made for man; they think there is proof, astronomical mainly, that it was made for man, I think there is evidence only, not proof, that it was made for him. It is too early, yet, to arrange the verdict, the returns are not all in. When they are all in, I think they will show that the world was made for man; but we must not hurry, we must patiently wait till they are all in.

Now as far as we have got, astronomy is on our side. Mr. Wallace has clearly shown this. He has clearly shown two things: that the world was made for man, and that the universe was made for the world—to stiddy it, you know. The astronomy part is settled, and cannot be challenged.

We come now to the geological part. This is the one where the evidence is not all in, yet. It is coming in, hourly, daily, coming in all the time, but naturally it comes with geological carefulness and deliberation, and we must not be impatient, we must not get excited, we must be calm, and wait. To lose our tranquillity will not hurry geology; nothing hurries geology.

It takes a long time to prepare a world for man, such a thing is not done in a day. Some of the great scientists, carefully ciphering the evidences furnished by geology, have arrived at the conviction that our world is prodigiously old, and they may be right, but Lord Kelvin is not of their opinion. He takes a cautious, conservative view, in order to be on the safe side, and feels sure it is not so old as they think. As Lord Kelvin is the highest authority in science now living, I think we must yield to him and accept his view. He does not concede that the world is more than a hundred million years old. He believes it is that old, but not older. Lyell believed that our race was introduced into the world 31,000 years ago, Herbert Spencer makes it 32,000. Lord Kelvin agrees with Spencer.

Very well. According to these figures it took 99,968,000 years to prepare the world for man, impatient as the Creator doubtless was to see him and admire him. But a large enterprise like this has to be conducted warily, painstakingly, logically. It was foreseen that man would have to have the oyster. Therefore the first preparation was made for the oyster. Very well, you cannot make an oyster out of whole cloth, you must make the oyster's ancestor first. This is not done in a day. You must make a vast variety of invertebrates, to start with— belemnites, trilobites, Jebusites, Amalekites, and that sort of fry, and put them to soak in a primary sea, and wait and see what will happen. Some will be a disapointment—the belemnites, the Ammonites and such; they will be failures, they will die out and become extinct, in the course of the nineteen million years covered by the experiment, but all is not lost, for the Amalekites will fetch the homestake; they will develop gradually into encrinites, and stalacites, and blatherskites, and one thing and another as the mighty ages creep on and the Archaean and the Cambrian Periods pile their lofty crags in the primordial seas, and at last the first grand stage in the preparation of the world for man stands completed, the oyster is done. An oyster has hardly any more reasoning power than a scientist has; and so it is reasonably certain that this one jumped to the conclusion that the nineteen million years was a preparation for him; but that would be just like an oyster, which is the most conceited animal there is, except man. And anyway, this one could not know, at that early date, that he was only an incident in a scheme, and that there was some more to the scheme, yet.

The oyster being achieved, the next thing to be arranged for in the preparation of the world for man was fish. Fish and coal—to fry it with. So the Old Silurian seas were opened up to breed the fish in, and at the same time the great work of building Old Red Sandstone mountains eighty thousand feet high to cold-storage their fossils in was begun. This latter was quite indispensable, for there would be no end of failures again, no end of extinctions—millions of them—and it would be cheaper and less trouble to can them in the rocks than keep tally of them in a book. One does not build the coal beds and eighty thousand feet of perpendicular Old Red Sandstone in a brief time—no, it took twenty million years. In the first place, a coal bed is a slow and troublesome and tiresome thing to construct. You have to grow prodigious forests of tree-ferns and reeds and calamites and such things in a marshy region; then you have to sink them under out of sight and let them rot; then you have to turn the streams on them, so as to bury them under several feet of sediment, and the sediment must have time to harden and turn to rock; next you must grow another forest on top, then sink it and put on another layer of sediment and harden it; then more forest and more rock, layer upon layer, three miles deep—ah, indeed it is a sickening slow job to build a coal-measure and do it right!

So the millions of years drag on; and meantime the fish culture is lazying along and frazzling out in a way to make a person tired. You have developed ten thousand kinds of fishes from the oyster; and come to look, you have raised nothing but fossils, nothing but extinctions. There is nothing left alive and progressive but a ganoid or two and perhaps half a dozen asteroids. Even the cat wouldn't eat such.

Still, it is no great matter; there is plenty of time, yet, and they will develop into something tasty before man is ready for them. Even a ganoid can be depended on for that, when he is not going to be called on for sixty million years.

The Paleozoic time limit having now been reached, it was necessary to begin the next stage in the preparation of the world for man, by opening up the Mesozoic Age and instituting some reptiles. For man would need reptiles. Not to eat, but to develop himself from. This being the most important detail of the scheme, a spacious liberality of time was set apart for it—thirty million years. What wonders followed! From the remaining ganoids and asteroids and alkaloids were developed by slow and steady and painstaking culture those stupendous saurians that used to prowl about the steamy world in those remote ages, with their snaky heads reared forty feet in the air and sixty feet of body and tail racing and thrashing after. All gone, now, alas—all extinct, except the little handful of Arkansawrians left stranded and lonely with us here upon this far-flung verge and fringe of time.

Yes, it took thirty million years and twenty million reptiles to get one that would stick long enough to develop into something else and let the scheme proceed to the next step.

Then the pterodactyl burst upon the world in all his impressive solemnity and grandeur, and all Nature recognized that the Cenozoic threshold was crossed and a new Period open for business, a new stage begun in the preparation of the globe for man. It may be that the pterodactyl thought the thirty million years had been intended as a preparation for himself, for there was nothing too foolish for a pterodactyl to imagine, but he was in error, the preparation was for man. Without doubt the pterodactyl attracted great attention, for even the least observant could see that there was the making of a bird in him. And so it turned out. Also the makings of a mammal, in time. One thing we have to say to his credit, that in the matter of picturesqueness he was the triumph of his Period; he wore wings and had teeth, and was a starchy and wonderful mixture altogether, a kind of long-distance premonitory symptom of Kipling's marine:

> 'E isn't one o' the reg'lar Line, nor 'e isn't one of the crew,
> 'E's a kind of a giddy harumfrodite—soldier an' sailor too!

From this time onward for nearly another thirty million years the preparation moved briskly. From the pterodactyl was developed the bird; from the bird the kangaroo, from the kangaroo the other marsupials; from these the mastodon, the megatherium, the giant sloth, the Irish elk, and all that crowd that you make useful and instructive fossils out of—then came the first great Ice Sheet, and they all retreated before it and crossed over the bridge at Bering Strait and wandered around over Europe and Asia and died. All except a few, to carry on the preparation with. Six Glacial Periods with two million years between Periods chased these poor orphans up and down and about the earth, from weather to weather—from tropic swelter at the poles to Arctic frost at the equator and back again and to and fro, they never knowing what kind of weather

was going to turn up next; and if ever they settled down anywhere the whole continent suddenly sank under them without
the least notice and they had to trade places with the fishes
and scramble off to where the seas had been, and scarcely a
dry rag on them; and when there was nothing else doing a
volcano would let go and fire them out from wherever they
had located. They led this unsettled and irritating life for
twenty-five million years, half the time afloat, half the time
aground, and always wondering what it was all for, they never
suspecting, of course, that it was a preparation for man and
had to be done just so or it wouldn't be any proper and harmonious place for him when he arrived.

And at last came the monkey, and anybody could see that
man wasn't far off, now. And in truth that was so. The monkey went on developing for close upon five million years, and
then turned into a man—to all appearances.

Such is the history of it. Man has been here 32,000 years.
That it took a hundred million years to prepare the world
for him is proof that that is what it was done for. I suppose
it is. I dunno. If the Eiffel Tower were now representing the
world's age, the skin of paint on the pinnacle-knob at its
summit would represent man's share of that age; and anybody would perceive that that skin was what the tower was
built for. I reckon they would, I dunno.

II   IN THE ANIMALS' COURT

1.

THE RABBIT. The testimony showed (1) that the Rabbit,
having declined to volunteer, was enlisted by compulsion, and
(2) deserted in the face of the enemy on the eve of battle.
Being asked if he had anything to say for himself before sentence of death should be passed upon him for violating the
military law forbidding cowardice and desertion, he said he
had not desired to violate that law, but had been obliged to
obey a higher law which took precedence of it and set it aside.
Being asked what law that was, he answered, "The law of
God, which denies courage to the rabbit."

Verdict of the Court. To be disgraced in the presence of the
army; stripped of his uniform; marched to the scaffold, bearing
a placard marked "Coward," and hanged.

2.

THE LION. The testimony showed that the Lion, by his splendid courage and matchless strength and endurance, saved the battle.

Verdict of the Court. To be given a dukedom, his statue to be set up, his name to be writ in letters of gold at the top of the roll in the Temple of Fame.

3.

THE FOX. The testimony showed that he had broken the divine law, "Thou shalt not steal." Being asked for his defense, he pleaded that he had been obliged to obey the divine law, "The Fox shall steal."

Verdict of the Court. Imprisonment for life.

4.

THE HORSE. The evidence showed that he had spent many days and nights, unwatched, in the paddock with the poultry, yet had triumphed over temptation.

Verdict of the Court. Let his name be honored; let his deed be praised throughout the land by public proclamation.

5.

THE WOLF. The evidence showed that he had transgressed the law, "Thou shalt not kill." In arrest of judgment, he pleaded the law of his nature.

Verdict of the Court. Death.

6.

THE SHEEP. The evidence showed that he had had manifold temptations to commit murder and massacre, yet had not yielded.

Verdict of the Court. Let his virtue be remembered forever.

7.

THE MACHINE.

THE COURT: Prisoner, it is charged and proven that you are poorly contrived and badly constructed. What have you to say to this?

ANSWER: I did not contrive myself, I did not construct myself.

THE COURT: It is charged and proven that you have moved when you should not have moved; that you have turned out of your course when you should have gone straight; that you have moved swiftly through crowds when the law and the public weal forbade a speed like that; that you leave a stench behind you wherever you go, and you persist in this, although you know it is improper and that other machines refrain from doing it. What have you to say to these things?

ANSWER: I am a machine. I am slave to the law of my make, I have to obey it, under all conditions. I do nothing, of myself. My forces are set in motion by outside influences, I never set them in motion myself.

THE COURT: You are discharged. Your plea is sufficient. You are a pretty poor thing, with some good qualities and some bad ones; but to attach personal merit to conduct emanating from the one set, and personal demerit to conduct emanating from the other set would be unfair and unjust. To a machine, that is—to a machine.

III   ZOLA'S LA TERRE

Have you read Zola's fearful book, *La Terre*? If so, did it not seem to you impossible, unbelievable that people such as those in that book are to be found in actual existence in any Christian land today? Were you able at any time, from the beginning to the end, to shake off the feeling that the tale was a hideous unreality, a tumultuous and ghastly nightmare, through which you were being whirled and buffeted helpless? Did the thought at any time come crashing into your dismayed mind, "What if this is no dream, but reality, and a picture of phases of life to be found here and there in all Christian lands!" That *is* a startling thought, isn't it? Well, I have just finished that book, and what I have said above indicates what happened to me: that is to say, chapter after chapter seemed to be only frightful inventions, crazy inventions of an obscene mind; then came the conviction that the tale was true, absolutely true, photographically true; and finally came that hair-lifting thought which I have mentioned.

But never mind about that, now. The thing that attracted my attention to the book was the rather doubtful statement, in a review, that its serial reproduction in a French newspaper had to be stopped, for the reason that the tale was so foul that the French people could not stand it. A story so foul that the French people could not stand it; why, that is like speaking of food that was so appetizing that no Frenchman would put up with it. Cold sarcasm like that revolts one; but I wanted to find out what the real reason was, so I sent for the book. Well, certainly, as a sustained effort in the way of filth,

and opulent variety of filthy material, and constant and con-
scientious attention to filthy detail, it does beat any French
book I ever saw before, and that is the very truth. There are
five hundred and eighteen pages in it; and if there is a single
page that would bear translation into English without the
use of blanks, I must have skipped it. The book calls a spade
a spade, all the time; and that is death to translation, of
course. However, it is only as a sustained effort that *La Terre*
stands at the head—or the other end—of French fiction. In
other French novels there are scattering situations—with the
proper French fidelity to detail—that are really more terrific
than any which this book can show.

Now what I am coming at, is this: are there any villages in
America whose people resemble the community described in
Zola's book? If one is asked this question suddenly, he will
feel a shock, and will answer, "Impossible!" But let him stop
and think. Perhaps he will not answer up so confidently, next
time. After reflection, after calling up particulars lying here
and there half-buried in his memory, he will probably grant
that there are in America villages that "resemble" that one, in
some ways, even in many ways. Well, that is a sufficient con-
cession. Will he go further, and name the state? And if he
will, will he name Massachusetts? Yes, under certain limita-
tions, he will name Massachusetts. He will proceed in this
way. He will say that without doubt Zola has suppressed the
bulk of his villagers—the worthy and the good—and has confined himself to the few and awful. If that was his way, then
it may be granted that he could have got material for a modified and yet dreadful enough *La Terre* out of the "few and
awful" minority findable in a Massachusetts village. When
you have granted that, in the case of Massachusetts, do you
feel daring enough to deny it in the case of any other state
in the Union? Hardly, I suppose.

It is very, very curious—the results that gradually come out,
when Zola's fearful book sets you to thinking. The first chapter
amazed you; when you read it, it seemed so grotesquely outside of the nineteenth-century possibilities. But reflection
changes your mind. You turn over your moss-grown facts, and
know that those circumstances have been repeated in America.
Once? Oh, no, several hundred thousand times. How far will
your thinking carry you? And what will you arrive at? This:
that there is hardly an accident or a conversation in the book
that has not repeated itself hundreds and hundreds of times

in America, and all over America. And then you will go still
further and remember some other things that have happened
in America—things still more hideously revolting than even
the most atrocious thing in Zola's volume.

How strange it is to reflect that that book is true. But it
is. You have to confess it at last. Then you are aware of a
grudge against him. Because he has exposed those odious
French people to you? No; but because he has exposed your
own people to you. You were asleep, and had forgotten; he
has waked you up. You owe him a grudge—and will keep it.

IV   THE INTELLIGENCE OF GOD

He made all things. There is not in the universe a thing, great
or small, which He did not make. He pronounced His work
"good." The word covers the whole of it; it puts the seal of
His approval upon each detail of it, it praises each detail of
it. We also approve and praise—with our mouths. We do it
loudly, we do it fervently—also judiciously. Judiciously. For
we do not enter into particulars. Daily we pour out freshets
of disapproval, dispraise, censure, passionate resentment, upon
a considerable portion of the work—but not with our mouths.
No, it is our acts that betray us, not our words. Our words
are all compliments, and they deceive Him. Without a doubt
they do. They make Him think we approve of all His works.

That is the way we argue. For ages we have taught ourselves
to believe that when we hide a disapproving fact, burying it
under a mountain of complimentary lies, He is not aware of
it, does not notice it, perceives only the compliments, and is
deceived. But is it really so? Among ourselves we concede that
acts speak louder than words, but we have persuaded ourselves
that in His case it is different; we imagine that all He cares
for is words—noise; that if we make the words pretty enough
they will blind Him to the acts that give them the lie.

But seriously, does anyone really believe that? Is it not a
daring affront to the Supreme Intelligence to believe such a
thing? Does any of us inordinately praise a mother's whole
family to her face, indiscriminately, and in that same moment
slap one of her children? Would not that act turn our inflamed
eulogy into nonsense? Would the mother be deceived? Would
she not be offended—and properly?

But see what we do in His case. We approve all His works,

we praise all His works, with a fervent enthusiasm—of words; and in the same moment we kill a fly, which is as much one of His works as is any other, and has been included and complimented in our sweeping eulogy. We not only kill the fly, but we do it in a spirit of measureless disapproval—even a spirit of hatred, exasperation, vindictiveness; and we regard that creature with disgust and loathing—which is the essence of contempt—and yet we have just been praising it, approving it, glorifying it. We have been praising it to its Maker, and now our act insults its Maker. The praise was dishonest, the act is honest; the one was wordy hypocrisy, the other is compact candor.

We hunt the fly remorselessly; also the flea, the rat, the snake, the disease germ and a thousand other creatures which He pronounced good, and was satisfied with, and which we loudly praise and approve—with our mouths—and then harry and chase and malignantly destroy, by wholesale.

Manifestly this is not well, not wise, not right. It breeds falsehood and sham. Would He be offended if we should change it and appear before Him with the truth in our mouths as well as in our acts? May we not, trustingly and without fear change our words and say:

"O Source of Truth, we have lied, and we repent. Hear us confess that which we have felt from the beginning of time, but have weakly tried to conceal from Thee: humbly we praise and glorify many of Thy works, and are grateful for their presence in our earth, Thy footstool, but not all of them."

That would be sufficient. It would not be necessary to name the exceptions.

V THE LOWEST ANIMAL*

In August, 1572, similar things were occurring in Paris and elsewhere in France. In this case it was Christian against Christian. The Roman Catholics, by previous concert, sprang a surprise upon the unprepared and unsuspecting Protestants, and butchered them by thousands—both sexes and all ages. This was the memorable St. Bartholomew's Day. At Rome the

* This was to have been prefaced by newspaper clippings which, apparently, dealt with religious persecutions in Crete. The clippings have been lost. They probably referred to the Cretan revolt of 1897. [B. DV.]

Pope and the Church gave public thanks to God when the happy news came.

During several centuries hundreds of heretics were burned at the stake every year because their religious opinions were not satisfactory to the Roman Church.

In all ages the savages of all lands have made the slaughtering of their neighboring brothers and the enslaving of their women and children the common business of their lives.

Hypocrisy, envy, malice, cruelty, vengefulness, seduction, rape, robbery, swindling, arson, bigamy, adultery, and the oppression and humiliation of the poor and the helpless in all ways have been and still are more or less common among both the civilized and uncivilized peoples of the earth.

For many centuries "the common brotherhood of man" has been urged—on Sundays—and "patriotism" on Sundays and weekdays both. Yet patriotism *contemplates the opposite of a common brotherhood.*

Woman's equality with man has never been conceded by any people, ancient or modern, civilized or savage.

I have been studying the traits and dispositions of the "lower animals" (so-called), and contrasting them with the traits and dispositions of man. I find the result humiliating to me. For it obliges me to renounce my allegiance to the Darwinian theory of the Ascent of Man from the Lower Animals; since it now seems plain to me that that theory ought to be vacated in favor of a new and truer one, this new and truer one to be named the *Descent* of Man from the Higher Animals.

In proceeding toward this unpleasant conclusion I have not guessed or speculated or conjectured, but have used what is commonly called the scientific method. That is to say, I have subjected every postulate that presented itself to the crucial test of actual experiment, and have adopted it or rejected it according to the result. Thus I verified and established each step of my course in its turn before advancing to the next. These experiments were made in the London Zoological Gardens, and covered many months of painstaking and fatiguing work.

Before particularizing any of the experiments, I wish to state one or two things which seem to more properly belong in this place than further along. This in the interest of clearness. The massed experiments established to my satisfaction certain generalizations, to wit:

1. That the human race is of one distinct species. It exhibits slight variations—in color, stature, mental caliber, and so on—due to climate, environment, and so forth; but it is a species by itself, and not to be confounded with any other.

2. That the quadrupeds are a distinct family, also. This family exhibits variations—in color, size, food preferences and so on; but it is a family by itself.

3. That the other families—the birds, the fishes, the insects, the reptiles, etc.—are more or less distinct, also. They are in the procession. They are links in the chain which stretches down from the higher animals to man at the bottom.

Some of my experiments were quite curious. In the course of my reading I had come across a case where, many years ago, some hunters on our Great Plains organized a buffalo hunt for the entertainment of an English earl—that, and to provide some fresh meat for his larder. They had charming sport. They killed seventy-two of those great animals; and ate part of one of them and left the seventy-one to rot. In order to determine the difference between an anaconda and an earl—if any—I caused seven young calves to be turned into the anaconda's cage. The grateful reptile immediately crushed one of them and swallowed it, then lay back satisfied. It showed no further interest in the calves, and no disposition to harm them. I tried this experiment with other anacondas; always with the same result. The fact stood proven that the difference between an earl and an anaconda is that the earl is cruel and the anaconda isn't; and that the earl wantonly destroys what he has no use for, but the anaconda doesn't. This seemed to suggest that the anaconda was not descended from the earl. It also seemed to suggest that the earl was descended from the anaconda, and had lost a good deal in the transition.

I was aware that many men who have accumulated more millions of money than they can ever use have shown a rabid hunger for more, and have not scrupled to cheat the ignorant and the helpless out of their poor servings in order to partially appease that appetite. I furnished a hundred different kinds of wild and tame animals the opportunity to accumulate vast stores of food, but none of them would do it. The squirrels and bees and certain birds made accumulations, but stopped when they had gathered a winter's supply, and could not be persuaded to add to it either honestly or by chicane. In order to bolster up a tottering reputation the ant pretended to store up supplies, but I was not deceived. I know the ant. These experiments convinced me that there is this difference between man and the higher animals: he is avaricious and miserly, they are not.

In the course of my experiments I convinced myself that among the animals man is the only one that harbors insults and injuries, broods over them, waits till a chance offers, then takes revenge. The passion of revenge is unknown to the higher animals.

Roosters keep harems, but it is by consent of their concubines; therefore no wrong is done. Men keep harems, but it is by brute force, privileged by atrocious laws which the other sex were allowed no hand in making. In this matter man occupies a far lower place than the rooster.

Cats are loose in their morals, but not consciously so. Man, in his descent from the cat, has brought the cat's looseness with him but has left the unconsciousness behind—the saving grace which excuses the cat. The cat is innocent, man is not. Indecency, vulgarity, obscenity—these are strictly confined to man; he invented them. Among the higher animals there is no trace of them. They hide nothing; they are not ashamed. Man, with his soiled mind, covers himself. He will not even enter a drawing room with his breast and back naked, so alive are he and his mates to indecent suggestion. Man is "The Animal that Laughs." But so does the monkey, as Mr. Darwin pointed out; and so does the Australian bird that is called the laughing jackass. No—Man is the Animal that Blushes. He is the only one that does it—or has occasion to.

At the head of this article we see how "three monks were burnt to death" a few days ago, and a prior "put to death with atrocious cruelty." Do we inquire into the details? No; or we should find out that the prior was subjected to unprintable mutilations. Man—when he is a North American Indian— gouges out his prisoner's eyes; when he is King John, with a nephew to render untroublesome, he uses a red-hot iron; when he is a religious zealot dealing with heretics in the Middle Ages, he skins his captive alive and scatters salt on his back; in the first Richard's time he shuts up a multitude of Jew families in a tower and sets fire to it; in Columbus's time he captures a family of Spanish Jews and—but *that* is not printable; in our day in England a man is fined ten shillings for beating his mother nearly to death with a chair, and another man is fined forty shillings for having four pheasant eggs in his possession without being able to satisfactorily explain how he

got them. Of all the animals, man is the only one that is cruel.
He is the only one that inflicts pain for the pleasure of doing
it. It is a trait that is not known to the higher animals. The
cat plays with the frightened mouse; but she has this excuse,
that she does not know that the mouse is suffering. The cat is
moderate—unhumanly moderate: she only scares the mouse,
she does not hurt it; she doesn't dig out its eyes, or tear off its
skin, or drive splinters under its nails—man-fashion; when she
is done playing with it she makes a sudden meal of it and
puts it out of its trouble. Man is the Cruel Animal. He is alone
in that distinction.

The higher animals engage in individual fights, but never in
organized masses. Man is the only animal that deals in that
atrocity of atrocities, War. He is the only one that gathers his
brethren about him and goes forth in cold blood and with
calm pulse to exterminate his kind. He is the only animal that
for sordid wages will march out, as the Hessians did in our
Revolution, and as the boyish Prince Napoleon did in the
Zulu war, and help to slaughter strangers of his own species
who have done him no harm and with whom he has no
quarrel.

Man is the only animal that robs his helpless fellow of his
country—takes possession of it and drives him out of it or destroys him. Man has done this in all the ages. There is not an
acre of ground on the globe that is in possession of its rightful
owner, or that has not been taken away from owner after
owner, cycle after cycle, by force and bloodshed.

Man is the only Slave. And he is the only animal who en-
slaves. He has always been a slave in one form or another, and
has always held other slaves in bondage under him in one way
or another. In our day he is always some man's slave for wages,
and does that man's work; and this slave has other slaves under
him for minor wages, and they do his work. The higher animals are the only ones who exclusively do their own work and
provide their own living.

Man is the only Patriot. He sets himself apart in his own
country, under his own flag, and sneers at the other nations,
and keeps multitudinous uniformed assassins on hand at heavy
expense to grab slices of other people's countries, and keep
them from grabbing slices of his. And in the intervals between
campaigns he washes the blood off his hands and works for
"the universal brotherhood of man"—with his mouth.

Man is the Religious Animal. He is the only Religious

Animal. He is the only animal that has the True Religion—several of them. He is the only animal that loves his neighbor as himself, and cuts his throat if his theology isn't straight. He has made a graveyard of the globe in trying his honest best to smooth his brother's path to happiness and heaven. He was at it in the time of the Caesars, he was at it in Mahomet's time, he was at it in the time of the Inquisition, he was at it in France a couple of centuries, he was at it in England in Mary's day, he has been at it ever since he first saw the light, he is at it today in Crete—as per the telegrams quoted above —he will be at it somewhere else tomorrow. The higher animals have no religion. And we are told that they are going to be left out, in the Hereafter. I wonder why? It seems questionable taste.

Man is the Reasoning Animal. Such is the claim. I think it is open to dispute. Indeed, my experiments have proven to me that he is the Unreasoning Animal. Note his history, as sketched above. It seems plain to me that whatever he is he is not a reasoning animal. His record is the fantastic record of a maniac. I consider that the strongest count against his intelligence is the fact that with that record back of him he blandly sets himself up as the head animal of the lot: whereas by his own standards he is the bottom one.

In truth, man is incurably foolish. Simple things which the other animals easily learn, he is incapable of learning. Among my experiments was this. In an hour I taught a cat and a dog to be friends. I put them in a cage. In another hour I taught them to be friends with a rabbit. In the course of two days I was able to add a fox, a goose, a squirrel and some doves. Finally a monkey. They lived together in peace; even affectionately.

Next, in another cage I confined an Irish Catholic from Tipperary, and as soon as he seemed tame I added a Scotch Presbyterian from Aberdeen. Next a Turk from Constantinople; a Greek Christian from Crete; an Armenian; a Methodist from the wilds of Arkansas; a Buddhist from China; a Brahman from Benares. Finally, a Salvation Army Colonel from Wapping. Then I stayed away two whole days. When I came back to note results, the cage of Higher Animals was all right, but in the other there was but a chaos of gory odds and ends of turbans and fezzes and plaids and bones and flesh —not a specimen left alive. These Reasoning Animals had disagreed on a theological detail and carried the matter to a Higher Court.

One is obliged to concede that in true loftiness of character, Man cannot claim to approach even the meanest of the Higher Animals. It is plain that he is constitutionally incapable of approaching that altitude; that he is constitutionally afflicted with a Defect which must make such approach forever impossible, for it is manifest that this defect is permanent in him, indestructible, ineradicable.

I find this Defect to be the Moral Sense. He is the only animal that has it. It is the secret of his degradation. It is the quality which enables him to do wrong. It has no other office. It is incapable of performing any other function. It could never have been intended to perform any other. Without it, man could do no wrong. He would rise at once to the level of the Higher Animals.

Since the Moral Sense has but the one office, the one capacity—to enable man to do wrong—it is plainly without value to him. It is as valueless to him as is disease. In fact, it manifestly is a disease. Rabies is bad, but it is not so bad as this disease. Rabies enables a man to do a thing which he could not do when in a healthy state: kill his neighbor with a poisonous bite. No one is the better man for having rabies. The Moral Sense enables a man to do wrong. It enables him to do wrong in a thousand ways. Rabies is an innocent disease, compared to the Moral Sense. No one, then, can be the better man for having the Moral Sense. What, now, do we find the Primal Curse to have been? Plainly what it was in the beginning: the infliction upon man of the Moral Sense; the ability to distinguish good from evil; and with it, necessarily, the ability to do evil; for there can be no evil act without the presence of consciousness of it in the doer of it.

And so I find that we have descended and degenerated, from some far ancestor—some microscopic atom wandering at its pleasure between the mighty horizons of a drop of water perchance—insect by insect, animal by animal, reptile by reptile, down the long highway of smirchless innocence, till we have reached the bottom stage of development—namable as the Human Being. Below us—nothing. Nothing but the Frenchman.

There is only one possible stage below the Moral Sense; that is the Immoral Sense. The Frenchman has it. Man is but little lower than the angels. This definitely locates him. He is between the angels and the French.

Man seems to be a rickety poor sort of a thing, any way you take him; a kind of British Museum of infirmities and inferiorities. He is always undergoing repairs. A machine that was as unreliable as he is would have no market. On top of his specialty—the Moral Sense—are piled a multitude of minor infirmities; such a multitude, indeed, that one may broadly call them countless. The higher animals get their teeth without pain or inconvenience. Man gets his through months and months of cruel torture; and at a time of life when he is but ill able to bear it. As soon as he has got them they must all be pulled out again, for they were of no value in the first place, not worth the loss of a night's rest. The second set will answer for a while, by being reinforced occasionally with rubber or plugged up with gold; but he will never get a set which can really be depended on till a dentist makes him one. This set will be called "false" teeth—as if he had ever worn any other kind.

In a wild state—a natural state—the Higher Animals have a few diseases; diseases of little consequence; the main one is old age. But man starts in as a child and lives on diseases till the end, as a regular diet. He has mumps, measles, whooping cough, croup, tonsillitis, diphtheria, scarlet fever, almost as a matter of course. Afterward, as he goes along, his life continues to be threatened at every turn: by colds, coughs, asthma, bronchitis, itch, cholera, cancer, consumption, yellow fever, bilious fever, typhus fevers, hay fever, ague, chilblains, piles, inflammation of the entrails, indigestion, toothache, earache, deafness, dumbness, blindness, influenza, chicken pox, cowpox, smallpox, liver complaint, constipation, bloody flux, warts, pimples, boils, carbuncles, abscesses, bunions, corns, tumors, fistulas, pneumonia, softening of the brain, melancholia and fifteen other kinds of insanity; dysentery, jaundice, diseases of the heart, the bones, the skin, the scalp, the spleen, the kidneys, the nerves, the brain, the blood; scrofula, paralysis, leprosy, neuralgia, palsy, fits, headache, thirteen kinds of rheumatism, forty-six of gout, and a formidable supply of gross and unprintable disorders of one sort and another. Also—but why continue the list? The mere names of the agents appointed to keep this shackly machine out of repair would hide him from sight if printed on his body in the smallest type known to the founder's art. He is but a

basket of pestilent corruption provided for the support and
entertainment of swarming armies of bacilli—armies commissioned to rot him and destroy him, and each army equipped
with a special detail of the work. The process of waylaying
him, persecuting him, rotting him, killing him, begins with
his first breath, and there is no mercy, no pity, no truce till he
draws his last one.

Look at the workmanship of him, in certain of its particulars. What are his tonsils for? They perform no useful
function; they have no value. They have no business there.
They are but a trap. They have but the one office, the one
industry: to provide tonsillitis and quinsy and such things for
the possessor of them. And what is the vermiform appendix
for? It has no value; it cannot perform any useful service. It is
but an ambuscaded enemy whose sole interest in life is to lie
in wait for stray grapeseeds and employ them to breed stran-
gulated hernia. And what are the male's mammals for? For
business, they are out of the question; as an ornament, they
are a mistake. What is his beard for? It performs no useful
function; it is a nuisance and a discomfort; all nations hate
it; all nations persecute it with the razor. And because it is a
nuisance and a discomfort, Nature never allows the supply
of it to fall short, in any man's case, between puberty and
the grave. You never see a man bald-headed on his chin. But
his hair! It is a graceful ornament, it is a comfort, it is the
best of all protections against certain perilous ailments, man
prizes it above emeralds and rubies. And because of these
things Nature puts it on, half the time, so that it won't stay.
Man's sight, smell, hearing, sense of locality—how inferior
they are. The condor sees a corpse at five miles; man has no
telescope that can do it. The bloodhound follows a scent that
is two days old. The robin hears the earthworm burrowing
his course under the ground. The cat, deported in a closed
basket, finds its way home again through twenty miles of
country which it has never seen.

Certain functions lodged in the other sex perform in a la-
mentably inferior way as compared with the performance of
the same functions in the Higher Animals. In the human
being, menstruation, gestation and parturition are terms which
stand for horrors. In the Higher Animals these things are hardly even inconveniences.

For style, look at the Bengal tiger—that ideal of grace,
beauty, physical perfection, majesty. And then look at Man—

that poor thing. He is the Animal of the Wig, the Trepanned Skull, the Ear Trumpet, the Glass Eye, the Pasteboard Nose, the Porcelain Teeth, the Silver Windpipe, the Wooden Leg— a creature that is mended and patched all over, from top to bottom. If he can't get renewals of his bric-a-brac in the next world, what will he look like?

He has just one stupendous superiority. In his intellect he is supreme. The Higher Animals cannot touch him there. It is curious, it is noteworthy, that no heaven has ever been offered him wherein his one sole superiority was provided with a chance to enjoy itself. Even when he himself has imagined a heaven, he has never made provision in it for intellectual joys. It is a striking omission. It seems a tacit confession that heavens are provided for the Higher Animals alone. This is matter for thought; and for serious thought. And it is full of a grim suggestion: that we are not as important, perhaps, as we had all along supposed we were.

The Great Dark

BEFORE IT HAPPENED
STATEMENT BY MRS. EDWARDS

WE WERE in no way prepared for this dreadful thing. We were a happy family, we had been happy from the beginning; we did not know what trouble was, we were not thinking of it nor expecting it.

My husband was thirty-five years old, and seemed ten years younger, for he was one of those fortunate people who by nature are overcharged with breezy spirits and vigorous health, and from whom cares and troubles slide off without making any impression. He was my ideal, and indeed my idol. In my eyes he was everything that a man ought to be, and in spirit and body beautiful. We were married when I was a girl of sixteen, and we now had two children, comely and dear little creatures: Jessie, eight years old, and Bessie, six.

The house had been in a pleasant turmoil all day, this 19th of March, for it was Jessie's birthday. Henry (my husband) had romped with the children till I was afraid he would tire them out and unfit them for their party in the evening, which was to be a children's fancy dress dance; and so I was glad at last in the edge of the evening he took them to our bedroom to show them the grandest of all the presents, the microscope. I allowed them fifteen minutes for this show. I would put the children into their costumes, then, and have them ready to receive their great flock of little friends and the accompanying parents. Henry would then be free to jot down in shorthand (he was a past master in that art) an essay which he was to read at the social club the next night. I would show the children to him in their smart costumes when the party should be over and the goodnight kisses due.

I left the three in a state of great excitement over the microscope, and at the end of the fifteen minutes I returned for the children. They and their papa were examining the wonders of a drop of water through a powerful lens. I delivered the children to a maid and they went away. Henry said, "I will take forty winks and then go to work. But I will make a new experiment with the drop of water first. Won't you please strengthen the drop with the merest touch of Scotch whisky and stir up the animals?"

Then he threw himself on the sofa and before I could speak he uttered a snore. That came of romping the whole day. In reaching for the whisky decanter I knocked off the one that contained brandy and it broke. The noise stopped the snore. I stooped and gathered up the broken glass hurriedly in a towel, and when I rose to put it out of the way he was gone. I dipped a broomstraw in the Scotch whisky and let a wee drop fall upon the glass slide where the water drop was, then I crossed to the glass door to tell him it was ready. But he had lit the gas and was at his table writing. It was the rule of the house not to disturb him when he was at work; so I went about my affairs in the picture gallery, which was our house's ballroom.

STATEMENT BY MR. EDWARDS

We were experimenting with the microscope. And pretty ignorantly. Among the little glass slides in the box we found one labeled "section of a fly's eye." In its center was faintly visible a dot. We put it under a low-power lens and it showed up like a fragment of honeycomb. We put it under a stronger lens and it became a window sash. We put it under the most powerful lens of all, then there was room in the field for only one pane of the several hundred. We were childishly delighted and astonished at the magnifying capacities of that lens, and said, "Now we can find out if there really are living animals in a drop of water, as the books say."

We brought some stale water from a puddle in the carriage house where some rotten hay lay soaking, sucked up a dropperful and allowed a tear of it to fall on a glass slide. Then we worked the screws and brought the lens down until it almost touched the water; then shut an eye and peered eagerly down through the barrel. A disappointment—nothing showed. Then we worked the screws again and made the lens touch the water. Another disappointment—nothing visible. Once more we worked the screws and projected the lens hard against the glass slide itself. Then we saw the animals! Not frequently, but now and then. For a time there would be a great empty blank; then a monster would enter one horizon of this great white sea made so splendidly luminous by the reflector and go plowing across and disappear beyond the opposite horizon. Others would come and go at intervals and disappear. The lens was pressing *against* the glass slide; therefore how could those bulky creatures crowd through between and not get stuck? Yet they swam with perfect freedom; it was plain that they had all the room and all the water that they needed. Then how unimaginably little they must be! Moreover, that wide circular sea which they were traversing was only a small part of our drop of stale water; it was not as big as the head of a pin; whereas the entire drop, flattened out on the glass, was as big around as a child's finger ring. If we could have gotten the whole drop under the lens we could have seen those gruesome fishes swim leagues and leagues before they dwindled out of sight at the further shore!

I threw myself on the sofa profoundly impressed by what I had seen, and oppressed with thinkings. An ocean in a drop of water—and unknown, uncharted, unexplored by man! By man, who gives all his time to the Africas and the poles, with this unsearched marvelous world right at his elbow. Then the Superintendent of Dreans appeared at my side, and we talked it over. He was willing to provide a ship and crew, but said, "It will be like any other voyage of the sort—not altogether a holiday excursion."

"That is all right; it is not an objection."

"You and your crew will be much diminished, as to size, but you need not trouble about that, as you will not be aware of it. Your ship itself, stuck upon the point of a needle, would not be discoverable except through a microscope of very high power."

"I do not mind these things. Get a crew of whalers. It will be well to have men who will know what to do in case we have trouble with those creatures."

"Better still if you avoid them."

"I shall avoid them if I can, for they have done me no harm, and I would not wantonly hurt any creature, but I shan't run from them. They have an ugly look, but I thank God I am not afraid of the ugliest that ever plowed a drop of water."

"You think so now, with your five feet eight, but it will be a different matter when the mote that floats in a sunbeam is Mont Blanc compared to you."

"It is no matter; you have seen me face dangers before—"

"Finish with your orders—the night is slipping away."

"Very well, then. Provide me a naturalist to tell me the names of the creatures we see; and let the ship be a comfortable one and perfectly appointed and provisioned, for I take my family with me."

Half a minute later (as it seemed to me), a hoarse voice broke on my ear:

"Topsails all—let go the lee brace—sheet home the stuns'le boom—hearty, now, and all together!"

I turned out, washed the sleep out of my eyes with a dash of cold water, and stepped out of my cabin, leaving Alice quietly sleeeping in her berth. It was a blustering night and dark, and the air was thick with a driving mist out of which the tall masts and bellying clouds of sail towered spectrally, faintly flecked here and there aloft by the smothered signal lanterns. The ship was heaving and wallowing in the heavy seas, and it was hard to keep one's footing on the moist deck. Everything was dimmed to obliteration, almost; the only thing sharply defined was the foamy mane of white water, sprinkled with phosphorescent sparks, which broke away from the lee bow. Men were within twenty steps of me, but I could not make out their figures; I only knew they were there by their voices. I heard the quartermaster report to the second mate, "Eight bells, sir."

"Very well—make it so."

Then I heard the muffled sound of the distant bell, followed by a far-off cry: "Eight bells and a cloudy morning—anchor watch turn out!"

I saw the glow of a match photograph a pipe and part of a face against the solid bank of darkness, and groped my way thither and found the second mate.

"What of the weather, mate?"

"I don't see that it's any better, sir, than it was the first day out, ten days ago; if anything it's worse—thicker and blacker, I mean. You remember the spitting snow flurries we had that night?"

"Yes."

"Well, we've had them again tonight. And hail and sleet besides, b'George! And here it comes again."

We stepped into the sheltering lee of the galley, and stood there listening to the lashing of the hail along the deck and the singing of the wind in the cordage.

The mate said, "I've been at sea thirty years, man and boy, but for a level ten-day stretch of unholy weather this bangs anything I ever struck, north of the Horn—if we are north of it. For I'm blest if I know where we are—do you?"

It was an embarrassing question. I had been asked it very confidentially by my captain, long ago, and had been able to state that I didn't know; and had been discreet enough not to go into any particulars; but this was the first time that any officer of the ship had approached me with the matter. I said, "Well, no, I'm not a sailor, but I am surprised to hear you say you don't know where we are."

He was caught. It was his turn to be embarrassed. First he began to hedge, and vaguely let on that perhaps he did know, after all; but he made a lame fist of it, and presently gave it up and concluded to be frank and take me into his confidence.

"I'm going to be honest with you, sir—and don't give me away." He put his mouth close to my ear and sheltered it against the howling wind with his hand to keep from having to shout, and said impressively, "Not only I don't know where we are, sir, but by God the captain himself don't know!"

I had met the captain's confession by pretending to be frightened and distressed at having engaged a man who was ignorant of his business; and then he had changed his note and told me he had only meant that he had lost his bearings in the thick weather—a thing which would rectify itself as soon as he could get a glimpse of the sun. But I was willing to let the mate tell me all he would, so long as I was not to "give it away."

"No, sir, he don't know where he is; lets on to, but he don't. I mean, he lets on to the crew, and his daughters, and young Phillips the purser, and of course to you and your family, but here lately he don't let on any more to the chief mate and me. And worried? I tell you he's worried plumb to his vitals."

"I must say I don't much like the look of this, Mr. Turner."

"Well, don't let on, sir; keep it to yourself—maybe it'll come out all right; hope it will. But you look at the facts—just look at the facts. We sail north—see? North-and-by-east-half-east, to be exact. Noon the fourth day out, heading for Sable Island —ought to see it, weather rather thin for *this* voyage. *Don't* see it. Think the dead reckoning ain't right, maybe. We bang straight along, all the afternoon. No Sable Island. *Damned if we didn't run straight over it!* It warn't there. What do you think of that?

"Dear me, it is awful—awful—if true."

"*If* true. Well it *is* true. True as anything that ever was, I take my oath on it. And then Greenland. We three banked our hopes on Greenland. Night before last we couldn't sleep for uneasiness; just anxiety, you know, to see if Greenland was going to be there. By the dead reckoning she was due to be in sight along anywhere from five to seven in the morning, if clear enough. But we stayed on deck all night. Of course two of us had no business there, and had to scuttle out of the way whenever a man came along, or they would have been suspicious. But five o'clock came, seven o'clock, eight o'clock, ten o'clock, and at last twelve—and then the captain groaned and gave in! He knew well enough that if there had been any Greenland left we'd have knocked a corner off of it long before that."

"This is appalling!"

"You may hunt out a bigger word than that and it won't cover it, sir. And Lord, to see the captain, gray as ashes, sweating and worrying over his chart all day yesterday and all day today, and spreading his compasses here and spreading them there, and getting suspicious of his chronometer, and damning the dead reckoning—just suffering death and taxes, you know, and me and the chief mate helping and suffering, and that purser and the captain's oldest girl spooning and cackling around, just in heaven! I'm a poor man, sir, but if I could buy out half of each of 'em's ignorance and put it together and make it a whole, blamed if I wouldn't put up my last nickel to do it, you hear me. Now—"

A wild gust of wind drowned the rest of his remark and smothered us in a fierce flurry of snow and sleet. He darted away and disappeared in the gloom, but first I heard his voice hoarsely shouting, "Turn out, all hands, shorten sail!"

There was a rush of feet along the deck, and then the gale brought the dimmed sound of far-off commands:

"Mizzen foretop halyards there—all clew garnets heave and away—now then, with a will—sheet home!"

And then the plaintive notes that told that the men were handling the kites:

> If you get there, before I do—
>   Hi—ho-o-o, roll a man down;
> If you get there before I do,
>   Oh, give a man time to roll a man down!

By and by all was still again. Meantime I had shifted to the other side of the galley to get out of the storm, and there Mr. Turner presently found me.

"That's a specimen," said he. "I've never struck any such weather anywheres. You are bowling along on a wind that's as steady as a sermon, and just as likely to last, and before you can say Jack Robinson the wind whips around from weather to lee, and if you don't jump for it, you'll have your canvas blown out of the catheads and sailing for heaven in rags and tatters. I've never seen anything to begin with it. But then I've never been in the middle of Greenland before—in a *ship*— middle of where it used to be, I mean. Would it worry you if I was to tell you something, sir?"

"Why, no, I think not. What is it?"

"Let me take a turn up and down, first, to see if anybody's in earshot." When he came back he said, "What should you think if you was to see a whale with hairy spider legs to it as long as the foretopgallant backstay and as big around as the mainmast?"

I recognized the creature; I had seen it in the microscope. But I didn't say so. I said, "I should think I had a little touch of the jimjams."

"The very thing I thought, so help me! It was the third day out, at a quarter to five in the morning. I was out astraddle of the bowsprit in the drizzle, bending on a scuttle butt, for I don't trust that kind of a job to a common sailor, when all of a sudden that creature plunged up out of the sea the way a porpoise does, not a hundred yards away—I saw two hundred and fifty feet of him and his fringes—and then he turned in the air like a triumphal arch, shedding Niagaras of water, and plunged head first under the sea with an awful swash of sound, and by that time we were close aboard him and in another ten yards we'd have hit him. It was my belief that he tried to hit us, but by the mercy of God he was out of practice. The look-out on the fo'c'sle was the only man around, and thankful I was, or there could have been a mutiny. He was asleep on the binnacle—they always sleep on the binnacle, it's the best place to see from—and it woke him up and he said, "Good land, what's that, sir?" and I said, "It's nothing, but it *might* have been, for any good a stump like you is for a lookout." I was pretty far gone, and said I was sick, and made him help me onto the fo'c'sle; and then I went straight off and took the pledge; for I had been going it pretty high for a week before we sailed, and I made up my mind that I'd rather go dry the rest of my life than see the like of that thing again."

"Well, I'm glad it was only the jimjams."

"Wait a minute, I ain't done. Of course I didn't enter it on the log—"

"Of course not—"

"For a man in his right mind don't put nightmares in the log. He only puts the word 'pledge' in, and takes credit for it if anybody inquires; and knows it will please the captain, and hopes it'll get to the owners. Well, two days later the chief mate took the pledge!"

"You don't mean it!"

"Sure as I'm standing here. I saw the word on the book. I didn't say anything, but I felt encouraged. Now then, listen to this: day before yesterday I'm dumm'd if the captain didn't take the pledge!"

"Oh, come!"

"It's a true bill—I take my oath. There was the word. Then we began to put this and that together, and next we begun to look at each other kind of significant and willing, you know; and of course giving the captain the preceedence, for it wouldn't become us to begin, and we nothing but mates. And so yesterday, sure enough, out comes the captain—and we called his hand. Said he was out astern in a snow flurry about dawn, and saw a creature shaped like a wood louse and as big as a turreted monitor, go racing by and tearing up the foam, in chase of a fat animal the size of an elephant and creased like a caterpillar—and saw it dive after it and disappear; and so he begun to prepare his soul for the pledge and break it to his entrails."

"It's terrible!"

"The pledge? You bet your bottom dollar. If I—"

"No, I don't mean the pledge; I mean it is terrible to be lost at sea among such strange, uncanny brutes."

"Yes, there's something in that, too, I don't deny it. Well, the thing that the mate saw was like one of these big long lubberly canal boats, and it was ripping along like the Empire Express; and the look of it gave him the cold shivers, and so he began to arrange his earthly affairs and go for the pledge."

"Turner, it is dreadful—dreadful. Still, good has been done; for these pledges—"

"Oh, they're off!"

"Off?"

"Cert'nly. Can't be jimjams; couldn't all three of us have them at once, it ain't likely. What do you want with a pledge when there ain't any occasion for it? There he goes!"

He was gone like a shot, and the night swallowed him up. Now all of a sudden, with the wind still blowing hard, the seas went down and the deck became as level as a billiard table! Were all the laws of Nature suspended? It made my flesh creep; it was like being in a haunted ship. Pretty soon the mate came back panting, and sank down on a cable tier, and said, "Oh, this is an awful life; I don't think we can stand it long. There's too many horrible in it. Let me pant a little, I'm in a kind of a collapse."

"What's the trouble?"

"Drop down by me, sir—I mustn't shout. There—now you're all right." Then he said sorrowfully, "I reckon we've got to take it again."

"Take what?"

"The pledge."

"Why?"

"Did you see that thing go by?"

"What thing?"

"A man."

"No. What of it?"

"This is four times that I've seen it; and the mate has seen it, and so has the captain. Haven't you ever seen it?"

"I suppose not. Is there anything extraordinary about it?"

"Extra-ordinary? Well, I should say!"

"How is it extraordinary?"

He said in an awed voice that was almost like a groan, "Like this, for instance: you put your hand on him and *he ain't there*."

"What do you mean, Turner?"

"It's as true as I'm sitting here, I wish I may never stir. The captain's getting morbid and religious over it, and says he wouldn't give a damn for ship and crew if that thing stays aboard."

"You curdle my blood. What is the man like? Isn't it just one of the crew, that you glimpse and lose in the dark?"

"You take note of *this*: it wears a broad slouch hat and a long cloak. Is that a whaler outfit? I'll ask you. A minute ago I was as close to him as I am to you; and I made a grab for him, and what did I get? A handful of air, that's all. There warn't a sign of him left."

"I do hope the pledge will dispose of it. It must be a work of the imagination, or the crew would have seen it."

"We're afraid they have. There was a deal of whispering going on last night in the middle watch. The captain dealt out grog, and got their minds on something else; but he is mighty uneasy, because of course he don't want you or your family to hear about that man, and would take my scalp if he knew what I'm doing now; and besides, if such a thing got a start with the crew, there'd be a mutiny, sure."

"I'll keep quiet, of course; still, I think it must be an output of imaginations overstrung by the strange fishes you think you saw; and I am hoping that the pledge—"

"I want to take it now. And I will."

"I'm witness to it. Now come to my parlor and I'll give you a cup of hot coffee and—"

"Oh, my goodness, there it is again! . . . It's gone. . . . Lord, it takes a body's breath. It's the jimjams I've got—I know it for sure. I want the coffee; it'll do me good. If you could help me a little, sir—I feel as weak as Sabbath grog."

We groped along the sleety deck to my door and entered, and there in the bright glare of the lamps sat (as I was half-expecting) the man of the long cloak and the slouch hat, on the sofa—my friend the Superintendent of Dreams. I was annoyed, for a moment, for of course I expected Turner to make a jump at him, get nothing, and be at once in a more miserable state than he already was. I reached for my cabin door and closed it, so that Alice might not hear the scuffle and get a fright. But there wasn't any. Turner went on talking, and took no notice of the Superintendent. I gave the Superintendent a grateful look; and it was an honest one, for this thing of making himself visible and scaring people could do harm.

"Lord, it's good to be in the light, sir," said Turner, rustling comfortably in his yellow oilskins. "It lifts a person's spirits right up. I've noticed that these cussed jimjam blatherskites ain't as apt to show up in the light as they are in the dark, except when you've got trouble in your attic pretty bad." Meantime we were dusting the snow off each other with towels. "You're mighty well fixed here, sir—chairs and carpets and rugs and tables and lamps and books and everything lovely, and so warm and comfortable and homey; and the roomiest parlor I ever struck in a ship, too. Land, hear the wind, don't she sing! And not a sign of motion! Rip goes the sleet again! —ugly, you bet! And here? Why, here it's only just the more cosier on account of it. Dern that jimjam, if I had him in here once I bet you I'd sweat him. Because I don't mind saying that I don't grab at him as earnest as I want to, outside there, and ain't as disappointed as I ought to be when I don't get him; but here in the light I ain't afraid of no jimjam."

It made the Superintendent of Dreams smile a smile that was full of pious satisfaction to hear him. I poured a steaming cup of coffee and handed it to Turner and told him to sit where he pleased and make himself comfortable and at home; and before I could interfere he had sat down in the Superintendent of Dream's lap!—no, sat down through him. It cost me a gasp, but only that, nothing more. The Superintendent of Dream's head was larger than Turner's, and surrounded it, and was a transparent spirit-head fronted with a transparent spirit-face; and this latter smiled at me as much as to say give myself no uneasiness, it is all right. Turner was smiling comfort and contentment at me at the same time, and the double result was very curious, but I could tell the smiles apart without trouble. The Superintendent of Dream's body enclosed Turner's, but I could see Turner through it, just as one sees objects through thin smoke. It was interesting and pretty.

Turner tasted his coffee and set the cup down in front of him with a hearty: "Now I call that prime! 'George, it makes me feel the way old Cap'n Jimmy Starkweather did, I reckon, the first time he tasted grog after he'd been off his allowance thr. years. The way of it was this. It was there in Fairhaven by New Bedford, away back in the old early whaling days before I was born; but I heard about it the first day I was born, and it was a ripe old tale then, because they keep only the one fleet of yarns in commission down New Bedford way, and don't ever restock and don't ever repair. And I came near hearing it in old Cap'n Jimmy's own presence once, when I was ten years old and he was ninety-two; but I didn't, because the man that asked Cap'n Jimmy to tell about it got crippled and the thing didn't materialize. It was Cap'n Jimmy that crippled him. Land, I thought I sh'd die! The very recollection of it—"

The very recollection of it so powerfully affected him that it shut off his speech and he put his head back and spread his jaws and laughed himself purple in the face. And while he was doing it the Superintendent of Dreams emptied the coffee into the slop bowl and set the cup back where it was before. When the explosion had spent itself Turner swabbed his face with his handkerchief and said, "There—that laugh has scoured me out and done me good; I hain't had such another one—well, not since I struck this ship, now that's sure. I'll whet up and start over."

He took up his cup, glanced into it, and it was curious to observe the two faces that were framed in the front of his head. Turner's was long and distressed; the Superintendent of Dream's was wide, and broken out of all shape with a convulsion of silent laughter. After a little, Turner said in a troubled way, "I'm dumm'd if I recollect drinking that."

I didn't say anything, though I knew he must be expecting me to say something. He continued to gaze into the cup a while, then looked up wistfully and said, "Of course I must have drunk it, but I'm blest if I can recollect whether I did or not. Lemme see. First you poured it out, then I sat down and put it before me here; next I took a sup and said it was good, and set it down and begun about old Cap'n Jimmy— and then—and then—" He was silent a moment, then said, "It's as far as I can get. It beats me. I reckon that after that I was so kind of full of my story that I didn't notice whether I—" He stopped again, and there was something almost pathetic about the appealing way in which he added, "But I did drink it, didn't I? You see me do it—didn't you?"

I hadn't the heart to say no.

"Why, yes, I think I did. I wasn't noticing particularly, but it seems to me that I saw you drink it—in fact, I am about certain of it."

I was glad I told the lie, it did him so much good, and so lightened his spirits, poor old fellow.

"Of course I done it! I'm such a fool. As a general thing I wouldn't care, and I wouldn't bother anything about it; but when there's jimjams around the least little thing makes a person suspicious, you know. If you don't mind, sir—thanks, ever so much." He took a large sup of the new supply, praised it, set the cup down—leaning forward and fencing it around with his arms, with a labored pretense of not noticing that he was doing that—then said:

"Lemme see—where was I? Yes. Well, it happened like this. The Washingtonian Movement started up in those old times, you know, and it was Father Matthew here and Father Matthew there and Father Matthew yonder—nothing but Father Matthew and temperance all over everywheres. And temperance societies? There was millions of them, and everybody joined and took the pledge. We had one in New Bedford. Every last whaler joined—captain, crew and all. All down to old Cap'n Jimmy. He was an old bach, his grog was his darling, he owned his ship and sailed her himself, he was independent, and he wouldn't give in. So at last they gave it up and quit pestering him. Time rolled along, and he got awful lonesome. There wasn't anybody to drink with, you see, and it got unbearable. So finally the day he sailed for Bering Strait he caved, and sent in his name to the society. Just as he was starting, his mate broke his leg and stopped ashore and he shipped a stranger in his place from down New York way.

This fellow didn't belong to any society, and he went aboard fixed for the voyage. Cap'n Jimmy was out three solid years; and all the whole time he had the spectacle of that mate whetting up every day and leading a life that was worth the trouble; and it nearly killed him for envy to see it. Made his mouth water, you know, in a way that was pitiful. Well, he used to get out on the peak of the bowsprit where it was private, and set there and cuss. It was his only relief from his sufferings. Mainly he cussed himself; but when he had used up all his words and couldn't think of any new rotten things to call himself, he would turn his vocabulary over and start fresh and lay into Father Matthew and give him down the banks; and then the society; and so put in his watch as satisfactory as he could. Then he would count the days he was out, and try to reckon up about when he could hope to get home and resign from the society and start in on an all-compensating drunk that would make up for lost time. Well, when he was out three thousand years—which was his estimate, you know, though really it was only three years—he came rolling down the home stretch with every rag stretched on his poles. Middle of winter, it was, and terrible cold and stormy. He made the landfall just at sundown and had to stand watch on deck all night of course, and the rigging was caked with ice three inches thick, and the yards was bearded with icicles five foot long, and the snow laid nine inches deep on the deck and hurricanes more of it being shoveled down onto him out of the skies. And so he plowed up and down all night, cussing himself and Father Matthew and the society, and doing it better than he ever done before; and his mouth was watering so, on account of the mate whetting up right in his sight all the time, that every cuss word come out damp, and froze solid as it fell, and in his insufferable indignation he would hit it a whack with his cane and knock it a hundred yards, and one of them took the mate in the mouth and fetched away a rank of teeth and lowered his spirits considerable. He made the dock just at early breakfast time and never waited to tie up, but jumped ashore with his jug in his hand and rushed for the society's quarters like a deer. He met the seckatary coming out and yelled at him, " 'I've resigned my membership! I give you just two minutes to scrape my name off your log, d'ye hear?'

"And then the seckatary told him he'd been blackballed three years before—hadn't ever been a member! Land, I can't hold in, it's coming again!"

He flung up his arms, threw his head back, spread his jaws,

and made the ship quake with the thunder of his laughter, while the Superintendent of Dreams emptied the cup again and set it back in its place. When Turner came out of his fit at last he was limp and exhausted, and sat mopping his tears away and breaking at times into little feebler and feebler barks and catches of expiring laughter. Finally he fetched a deep sigh of comfort and satisfaction, and said, "Well, it does do a person good, no mistake—on a voyage like this. I reckon—"

His eye fell on the cup. His face turned a ghastly white.

"By God she's empty again!"

He jumped up and made a sprawling break for the door. I was frightened; I didn't know what he might do—jump overboard, maybe. I sprang in front of him and barred the way, saying, "Come, Turner, be a man, be a man! don't let your imagination run away with you like this;" and over his shoulder I threw a pleading look at the Superintendent of Dreams, who answered my prayer and refilled the cup from the coffee urn.

"Imagination you call it, sir! Can't I see—with my own eyes? Let me go—don't stop me—I can't stand it, I can't stand it!"

"Turner, be reasonable—you know perfectly well your cup isn't empty, and hasn't been."

That hit him. A dim light of hope and gratitude shone in his eye, and he said in a quivery voice, "Say it again—and say it's true. Is it true? Honor bright—you wouldn't deceive a poor devil that's—"

"Honor bright, man, I'm not deceiving you—look for yourself."

Gradually he turned a timid and wary glance toward the table; then the terror went out of his face, and he said humbly, "Well, you see, I reckon I hadn't quite got over thinking it happened the first time, and so maybe without me knowing it, that made me kind of suspicious that it would happen again, because the jimjams make you untrustful that way; and so, sure enough, I didn't half-look at the cup, and just jumped to the conclusion it had happened." And talking so, he moved toward the sofa, hesitated a moment, and then sat down in that figure's body again. "But I'm all right, now, and I'll just shake these feelings off and be a man, as you say."

The Superintendent of Dreams separated himself and moved along the sofa a foot or two away from Turner. I was glad of that; it looked like a truce. Turner swallowed his cup of coffee; I poured another; he began to sip it, the pleasant influence worked a change, and soon he was a rational man again, and comfortable. Now a sea came aboard, hit our deckhouse a stunning thump, and went hissing and seething aft.

"Oh, that's the ticket," said Turner, "the dumm'est weather that ever I went pleasure-excursioning in. An l how did it get aboard? You answer me that: there ain't any motion to the ship. These mysteriousnesses—well, they just give me the cold shudders. And that reminds me. Do you mind my calling your attention to another peculiar thing or two? On conditions as before—solid secrecy, you know."

"I'll keep it to myself. Go on."

"The Gulf Stream's gone to the devil!"

"What do you mean?"

"It's the fact, I wish I may never die. From the day we sailed till now, the water's been the same temperature right along, I'll take my oath. The Gulf Stream don't exist any more; she's gone to the devil."

"It's incredible, Turner! You make me gasp."

"Gasp away, if you want to; if things go on so, you ain't going to forget how for want of practice. It's the wooliest voyage, take it by and large—why, look here! You are a landsman, and there's no telling what a landsman can't overlook if he tries. For instance, have you noticed that the nights and days are exactly alike, and you can't tell one from tother except by keeping tally?"

"Why, yes, I have noticed it in a sort of indifferent general way, but—"

"Have you kept a tally, sir?"

"No, it didn't occur to me to do it."

"I thought so. Now you know, you couldn't keep it in your head, because you and your family are free to sleep as much as you like, and as it's always dark, you sleep a good deal, and you are pretty irregular, naturally. You've all been a little seasick from the start—tea and toast in your own parlor here—no regular time—order it as each of you pleases. You see? You don't go down to meals—they would keep tally for you. So you've lost your reckoning. I noticed it an hour ago."

"How?"

"Well, you spoke of tonight. It ain't tonight at all; it's just noon, now."

"The fact is, I don't believe I have often thought of it's being day, since we left. I've got into the habit of considering it night all the time; it's the same with my wife and the children."

"There it is, you see. Mr. Edwards, it's perfectly awful; now ain't it, when you come to look at it? Always night—and such dismal nights, too. It's like being up at the pole in the winter-time. And I'll ask you to notice another thing: this sky is as empty as my sou'wester there."

"Empty?"

"Yes, sir. I know it. You can't get up a day, in a Christian country, that's so solid black the sun can't make a blurry glow of some kind in the sky at high noon—now can you?"

"No, you can't."

"Have you ever seen a suspicion of any such a glow in this sky?"

"Now that you mention it, I haven't."

He dropped his voice and said impressively, "Because there ain't any sun. She's gone where the Gulf Stream twineth."

"Turner! Don't talk like that."

"It's confidential or I wouldn't. And the moon. She's at the full—by the almanac she is. Why don't she make a blur? Because there ain't any moon. And moreover—you might rake this on-completed sky a hundred year with a dragnet and you'd never scoop a star! Why? Because there ain't any. Now then, what is your opinion about all this?"

"Turner, it's so gruesome and creepy that I don't like to think about it—and I haven't any. What is yours?"

He said, dismally, "That the world has come to an end. Look at it yourself. Just look at the facts. Put them together and add them up, and what have you got? No Sable Island; no Greenland; no Gulf Stream; no day, no proper night; weather that don't jibe with any sample known to the Bureau; animals that would start a panic in any menagerie, chart no more use than a horseblanket, and the heavenly bodies gone to hell! And on top of it all, that jimjam that I've put my hand on more than once and he warn't there—I'll swear it. The ship's bewitched. You don't believe in the jim, and I've sort of lost faith myself, here in the bright light; but if this cup of coffee was to—"

The cup began to glide slowly away, along the table. The hand that moved it was not visible to him. He rose slowly to his feet and stood trembling as if with an ague, his teeth knocking together and his glassy eyes staring at the cup. It slid on and on, noiseless; then it rose in the air, gradually reversed itself, poured its contents down the Superintendent's throat —I saw the dark stream trickling its way down through his hazy breast—then it returned to the table, and without sound of contact, rested there. The mate continued to stare at it for as much as a minute; then he drew a deep breath, took up his sou'wester, and without looking to the right or the left, walked slowly out of the room like one in a trance, muttering, "I've got them—I've had the proof."

I said, reproachfully, "Superintendent, why do you do that?"

"Do what?"

"Play these tricks."

"What harm is it?"

"Harm? It could make that poor devil jump overboard."

"No, he's not as far gone as that."

"For a while he was. He is a good fellow, and it was a pity to scare him so. However, there are other matters that I am more concerned about just now."

"Can I help?"

"Why, yes, you can; and I don't know anyone else that can."

"Very well, go on."

"By the dead reckoning we have come twenty-three hundred miles."

"The actual distance is twenty-three-fifty."

"Straight as a dart in the one direction—mainly."

"Apparently."

"Why do you say apparently? Haven't we come straight?"

"Go on with the rest. What were you going to say?"

"This. Doesn't it strike you that this is a pretty large drop of water?"

"No. It is about the usual size—six thousand miles across."

"Six thousand miles!"

"Yes."

"Twice as far as from New York to Liverpool?"

"Yes."

"I must say it is more of a voyage than I counted on. And we are not a great deal more than halfway across, yet. When shall we get in?"

"It will be some time yet."

"That is not very definite. Two weeks?"

"More than that."

I was getting a little uneasy.

"But how much more? A week?"

"All of that. More, perhaps."

"Why don't you tell me? A month more, do you think?"

"I am afraid so. Possibly two—possibly longer, even."

I was getting seriously disturbed by now.

"Why, we are sure to run out of provisions and water."

"No, you'll not. I've looked out for that. It is what you are loaded with."

"Is that so? How does that come?"

"Because the ship is chartered for a voyage of discovery. Ostensibly she goes to England, takes aboard some scientists, then sails for the South Pole."

"I see. You are deep."

"I understand my business."

I turned the matter over in my mind a moment, then said, "It is more of a voyage than I was expecting, but I am not of a worrying disposition, so I do not care, so long as we are not going to suffer hunger and thirst."

"Make yourself easy, as to that. Let the trip last as long as it may, you will not run short of food and water, I go bail for that."

"All right, then. Now explain this riddle to me. Why is it always night?"

"That is easy. All of the drop of water is outside the luminous circle of the microscope except one thin and delicate rim of it. We are in the shadow; consequently in the dark."

"In the shadow of what?"

"Of the brazen end of the lens holder."

"How can it cover such a spread with its shadow?"

"Because it is several thousand miles in diameter. For dimensions, that is nothing. The glass slide which it is pressing against, and which forms the bottom of the ocean we are sailing upon, is thirty thousand miles long, and the length of the miscroscope barrel is a hundred and twenty thousand. Now then, if—"

"You make me dizzy. I—"

"If you should thrust that glass slide through what you call the 'great' globe, eleven thousand miles of it would stand out on each side—it would be like impaling an orange on a table knife. And so—"

"It gives me the headache. Are these the fictitious proportions which we and our surroundings and belongings have acquired by being reduced to microscopic objects?"

"They are the proportions, yes—but they are in any way fictitious. You do not notice that you yourself are in any way diminished in size, do you?"

"No, I am my usual size, as far as I can see."

"The same with the men, the ship and everything?"

"Yes—all natural."

"Very good; nothing but the laws and conditions have undergone a change. You came from a small and very insignificant world. The one you are in now is proportioned according to microscopic standards—that is to say, it is inconceivably stupendous and imposing."

It was food for thought. There was something overpowering in the situation, something sublime. It took me a while to shake off the spell and drag myself back to speech. Presently I said, "I am content; I do not regret the voyage—far from it. I would not change places with any man in that cramped little world. But tell me—is it always going to be dark?"

"Not if you ever come into the luminous circle under the lens. Indeed you will not find *that* dark!"

"If we ever. What do you mean by that? We are making steady good time; we are cutting across this sea on a straight course."

"Apparently."

"There is no apparently about it."

"You might be going around in a small and not rapidly widening circle."

"Nothing of the kind. Look at the telltale compass over your head."

"I see it."

"We changed to this easterly course to satisfy everybody but me. It is a pretense of aiming for England—in a drop of water! Have you noticed that needle before?"

"Yes, a number of times."

"Today, for instance?"

"Yes—often."

"Has it varied a jot?"

"Not a jot."

"Hasn't it always kept the place appointed for it—from the start?"

"Yes, always."

"Very well. First we sailed a northerly course; then tilted easterly; and now it is more so. How is *that* going around in a circle?"

He was silent. I put it at him again. He answered with lazy indifference, "I merely threw out the suggestion."

"All right, then; cornered; let it stand at that. Whenever you happen to think of an argument in support of it, I shall be glad to hear about it."

He did not like that very well, and muttered something about my being a trifle airy. I retorted a little sharply, and followed it up by finding fault with him again for playing tricks on Turner. He said Turner called him a blatherskite. I said, "No matter; you let him alone, from this out. And moreover, stop appearing to people—stop it entirely."

His face darkened. He said, "I would advise you to moderate your manner. I am not used to it, and I am not pleased with it."

The rest of my temper went, then. I said, angrily, "You may like it or not, just as you choose. And moreover, if my style doesn't suit you, you can end the dream as soon as you please—right now, if you like."

He looked me steadily in the eye for a moment, then said, with deliberation, "The dream? Are you quite sure it is a dream?"

It took my breath away.

"What do you mean? Isn't it a dream?"

He looked at me in that same way again; and it made my blood chilly, this time. Then he said, "I give you ten years to get over that superstition in!"

It was as if he had hit me, it stunned me so. Still looking at me his lip curled itself into a mocking smile, and he wasted away like a mist and disappeared.

I sat a long time thinking uncomfortable thoughts.

We are strangely made. We think we are wonderful creatures. Part of the time we think that, at any rate. And during that interval we consider with pride our mental equipment, with its penetration, its power of analysis, its ability to reason out clear conclusions from confused facts, and all the lordly rest of it; and then comes a rational interval and disenchants us. Disenchants us and lays us bare to ourselves, and we see that intellectually we are really no great things; that we seldom really know the thing we think we know; that our best-built certainties are but sand-houses and subject to damage from any wind of doubt that blows.

So little a time before, I knew that this voyage was a dream, and nothing more; a wee little puff or two of doubt had blown against that certainty, unhelped by fact or argument, and already it was dissolving away. It seemed an incredible thing, and it hurt my pride of intellect, but it had to be confessed.

When I came to consider it, these ten days had been such intense realities!—so intense that by comparison the life I had lived before them seemed distant, indistinct, slipping away and fading out in a far perspective—exactly as a dream does when you sit at breakfast trying to call back its details. I grew steadily more and more nervous and uncomfortable—and a little frightened, though I would not quite acknowledge this to myself.

Then came this disturbing thought: if this transformation goes on, how am I going to conceal it from my wife? Suppose she should say to me, "Henry, there is something the matter with you, you are acting strangely; something is on your mind that you are concealing from me; tell me about it, let me help you." What answer could I make?

I was *bound* to act strangely if this went on—bound to bury myself in deeps of troubled thought; I should not be able to help it. She had a swift eye to notice, where her heart was concerned, and a sharp intuition, and I was an impotent poor thing in her hands when I had things to hide and she had struck the trail.

I have no large amount of fortitude, staying power. When there is a fate before me I cannot rest easy until I know what it is. I am not able to wait. I want to know, right way. So, I would call Alice, now, and take the consequences. If she drove me into a corner and I found I could not escape, I would act according to my custom—come out and tell her the truth. She had a better head than mine, and a surer instinct in grouping facts and getting their meaning out of them. If I was drifting into dangerous waters, now, she would be sure to detect it and as sure to set me right and save me. I would call her, and keep out of the corner if I could; if I couldn't, why—I couldn't, that is all.

She came, refreshed with sleep, and looking her best self; that is to say, looking like a girl of nineteen, not a matron of twenty-five; she wore a becoming wrapper, or tea gown, or whatever it is called, and it was trimmed with ribbons and limp stuff—lace, I suppose; and she had her hair balled up and nailed to its place with a four-pronged tortoise-shell comb. She brought a basket of pink and gray crewels with her, for she was crocheting a jacket—for the cat, probably, judging by the size of it. She sat down on the sofa and set the basket on the table, expecting to have a chance to get to work by and by; not right away, because a kitten was curled up in it asleep, fitting its circle snugly, and the repose of the children's kittens was a sacred thing and not to be disturbed. She said, "I noticed that there was no motion—it was what waked me, I think—and I got up to enjoy it, it is such a rare thing."

"Yes, rare enough, dear; we do have the most unaccountably strange weather."

"Do you think so, Henry? Does it seem strange weather to you?"

She looked so earnest and innocent that I was rather startled, and a little in doubt as to what to say. Any sane person could see that it was perfectly devilish weather and crazy beyond imagination, and so how could she feel uncertain about it?"

"Well, Alice, I may be putting it too strong, but I don't think so; I think a person may call our weather by any hard name he pleases and be justified."

"Perhaps you are right, Henry. I have heard the sailors talk the same way about it, but I did not think that that meant much, they speak so extravagantly about everything. You are not always extravagant in your speech—often you are, but not always—and so it surprised me a little to hear you." Then she added tranquilly and musingly, "I don't remember any different weather."

It was not quite definite.

"You mean on *this* voyage, Alice."

"Yes, of course. Naturally. I haven't made any other."

She was softly stroking the kitten—and apparently in her right mind. I said cautiously, and with seeming indifference, "You mean you haven't made any other this year. But the time we went to Europe—well, that was very different weather."

"The time we went to Europe, Henry?"

"Certainly, certainly—when Jessie was a year old."

She stopped stroking the kitty, and looked at me inquiringly. "I don't understand you, Henry."

She was not a joker, and she was always truthful. Her remark blew another wind of doubt upon my wasting sand-edifice of certainty. Had I only *dreamed* that we went to Europe? It seemed a good idea to put this thought into words.

"Come, Alice, the first thing you know you will be imagining that we went to Europe in a dream."

She smiled, and said, "Don't let me spoil it, Henry, if it is pleasant to you to think we went. I will consider that we did go, and that I have forgotten it."

"But, Alice dear, we *did* go!"

"But, Henry dear, we *didn't* go!"

She had a good head and a good memory, and she was always truthful. My head had been injured by a fall when I was a boy, and the physicians had said at the time that there could be ill effects from it some day. A cold wave struck me, now; perhaps the effects had come. I was losing confidence in the European trip. However, I thought I would make another try.

"Alice, I will give you a detail or two; then maybe you will remember."

"A detail or two from the dream?"

"I am not at all sure that it was a dream; and five minutes ago I was sure that it wasn't. It was seven years ago. We went over in the *Batavia*. Do you remember the *Batavia?*"

"I don't, Henry."

"Captain Moreland. Don't you remember him?"

"To me he is a myth, Henry."

"Well, it beats anything. We lived two or three months in London, then six weeks in a private hotel in George Street, Edinburgh—Veitch's. Come!"

"It sounds pleasant, but I have never heard of these things before, Henry."

"And Dr. John Brown, of *Rab and His Friends*—you were ill, and he came every day; and when you were well again he still came every day and took us all around while he paid his visits, and we waited in his carriage while he prescribed for his patients. And he was so dear and lovely. You *must* remember all that, Alice."

"None of it, dear; it is only a dream."

"Why, Alice, have you ever had a dream that remained as distinct as that, and which you could remember so long?"

"So long? It is more than likely that you dreamed it last night."

"No indeed! It has been in my memory seven years."

"Seven years in a dream, yes—it is the way of dreams. They put seven years into two minutes, without any trouble—isn't it so?"

I had to acknowledge that it was.

"It seems almost as if it couldn't have been a dream, Alice; it seems as if you ought to remember it."

"Wait! It begins to come back to me." She sat thinking a while, nodding her head with satisfaction from time to time. At last she said, joyfully, "I remember almost the whole of it, now."

"Good!"

"I am glad I got it back. Ordinarily I remember my dreams very well; but for some reason this one—"

"*This* one, Alice? Do you really consider it a dream, yet?"

"I don't consider anything about it, Henry, I know it; I know it positively."

The conviction stole through me that she must be right, since she felt so sure. Indeed I almost knew she was. I was privately becoming ashamed of myself now, for mistaking a clever illusion for a fact. So I gave it up, then, and said I would let it stand as a dream. Then I added, "It puzzles me; even now it seems almost as distinct as the microscope."

"Which microscope?"

"Well, Alice, there's only the one."

"Very well, which one is *that?*"

"Bother it all, the one we examined this ocean in, the other day."

"Where?"

"Why, at home—of course."

"What home?"

"Alice, it's provoking—why, our home. In Springport."

"Dreaming again. I've never heard of it."

That was stupefying. There was no need of further beating about the bush; I threw caution aside, and came out frankly.

"Alice, what do you call the life we are leading in this ship? Isn't it a dream?"

She looked at me in a puzzled way and said, "A dream, Henry? Why should I think that?"

"Oh, dear me, I don't know! I thought I did, but I don't. Alice, haven't we ever had a home? Don't you remember one?"

"Why, yes—three. That is, dream-homes, not real ones. I have never regarded them as realities."

"Describe them."

She did it, and in detail; also our life in them. Pleasant enough homes, and easily recognizable by me. I could also recognize an average of two out of seven of the episodes and incidents which she threw in. Then I described the home and the life which (as it appeared to me) we had so recently left. She recognized it—but only as a dream-home. She remembered nothing about the microscope and the children's party. I was in a corner; but it was not the one which I had arranged for.

"Alice, if those were dream-houses, how long have you been in this ship? You say this is the only voyage you have ever made."

"I don't know. I don't remember. It *is* the only voyage we have made—unless breaking it to pick up this crew of strangers in place of the friendly dear men and officers we had sailed with so many years makes two voyages of it. How I do miss them—Captain Hall, and Williams the sailmaker, and Storrs the chief mate, and—"

She choked up, and the tears began to trickle down her cheeks. Soon she had her handkerchief out and was sobbing.

I realized that I remembered those people perfectly well. Damnation! I said to myself, are we real creatures in a real world, all of a sudden, and have we been feeding on dreams in an imaginary one since nobody knows when—or how is it? My head was swimming.

"Alice! Answer me this. Do you know the Superintendent of Dreams?"

"Certainly."

"Have you seen him often?"

"Not often, but several times."

"When did you see him first?"

"The time that Robert the captain's boy was eaten."

"Eaten?"

"Yes. Surely you haven't forgotten that?"

"But I have, though. I never heard of it before."

Her face was full of reproach.

"I am sorry, if that is so. He was always good to you. If you are jesting, I do not think it is in good taste."

"Now don't treat me like that, Alice, I don't deserve it. I am not jesting, I am in earnest. I mean the boy's memory no offense, but although I remember him I do not remember the circumstance—I swear it. Who ate him?"

"Do not be irreverent, Henry, it is out of place. It was not a *who*, at all."

"What then—a *which*?"

"Yes."

"What kind of a which?"

"A spider-squid. *Now* you remember it I hope."

"Indeed and deed and double-deed I don't, Alice, and it is the real truth. Tell me about it, please."

"I suppose you see, now, Henry, what your memory is worth. You can remember dream-trips to Europe well enough, but things in real life—even the most memorable and horrible things—pass out of your memory in twelve years. There is something the matter with your mind."

It was very curious. How *could* I have forgotten that tragedy? It must have happened; she was never mistaken in her facts, and she never spoke with positiveness of a thing which

she was in any degree uncertain about. And this tragedy—
twelve years ago—

"Alice, how long have we been in this ship?"

"Now how can I know, Henry? It goes too far back. Always,
for all I know. The earliest thing I can call to mind was
Papa's death by the sun heat and Mama's suicide the same
day. I was four years old, then. Surely you must remember
that, Henry.

"Why, you must remember that we were in the edge of a
great white glare once for a little while—a day, or maybe two
days—only a little while, I think, but I remember it, because
it was the only time I was ever out of the dark, and there
was a great deal of talk of it for long afterward—why, Henry,
you must remember a wonderful thing like that."

"Wait. Let me think." Gradually, detail by detail the whole
thing came back to me; and with it the boy's adventure with
the spider-squid; and then I recalled a dozen other incidents,
which Alice verified as incidents of our ship-life, and said I
had set them forth correctly.

It was a puzzling thing—my freaks of memory; Alice's, too.
By testing, it was presently manifest that the vacancies in
my ship-life memories were only apparent, not real; a few words by
way of reminder enabled me to fill them up, in almost all
cases, and give them clarity and vividness. What had caused
these temporary lapses? Didn't these very lapses indicate that
the ship-life was a dream, and not real?

It made Alice laugh.

I did not see anything foolish in it, or anything to laugh at,
and I told her so. And I reminded her that her own memory
was as bad as mine, since many and many a conspicuous episode of our land-life was gone from her, even so striking an
incident as the water-drop exploration with the microscope—

It made her shout.

I was wounded; and said that if I could not be treated with
respect I would spare her the burden of my presence and
conversation. She stopped laughing, at once, and threw her
arms about my neck. She said she would not have hurt me
for the world, but she supposed I was joking; it was quite
natural to think I was not in earnest in talking gravely about
this and that and the other dream-phantom as if it were a
reality.

"But Alice I was in earnest, and I am in earnest. Look at
it—examine it. If the land-life was a dream-life, how is it that
you remember so much of it exactly as I remember it?"

She was amused again, inside—I could feel the quiver; but
there was no exterior expression of it, for she did not want to
hurt me again.

"Dear heart, throw the whole matter aside! Stop puzzling
over it; it isn't worth it. It is perfectly simple. It is true that I
remember a little of that dream-life just as you remember it—
but that is an accident; the rest of it—and by far the largest
part—does not correspond with your recollections. And how
could it? People can't be expected to remember each other's
dreams, but only their own. You have put me into your land-
dreams a thousand times, but I didn't always know I was there;
so how could I remember it? Also I have put you into my
land-dreams a thousand times when you didn't know it—and
the natural result is that when I name the circumstances you
don't always recall them. But how different it is with this real
life, this genuine life in the ship! Our recollections of it are
just alike. You have been forgetting episodes of it today—I
don't know why; it has surprised me and puzzled me—but the
lapse was only temporary; your memory soon rallied again.
Now it hasn't rallied in the case of land-dreams of mine—in
most cases it hasn't. And it's not going to, Henry. You can be
sure of that."

She stopped, and tilted her head up in a thinking attitude
and began to unconsciously tap her teeth with the ivory knob
of a crochet needle. Presently she said, "I think I know what
is the matter. I have been neglecting you for ten days while
I have been grieving for our old shipmates and pretending to
be seasick so that I might indulge myself with solitude; and
here is the result—you haven't been taking exercise enough."

I was glad to have a reason—any reason that would excuse
my memory—and I accepted this one, and made confession.
There was no truth in the confession, but I was already getting
handy with these evasions. I was a little sorry for this, for she
had always trusted my word, and I had honored this trust by
telling her the truth many a time when it was a sharp sacrifice
to me to do it.

She looked me over with gentle reproach in her eye, and
said, "Henry, how can you be so naughty? I watch you so
faithfully and make you take such good care of your health
that you owe me the grace to do my office for me when for
any fair reason I am for a while not on guard. When have you
boxed with George last?"

What an idea it was! It was a good place to make a mistake,
and I came near to doing it. It was on my tongue's end to say

that I had never boxed with anyone; and as for boxing with a colored manservant—and so on; but I kept back my remark, and in place of it tried to look like a person who didn't know what to say. It was easy to do, and I probably did it very well.

"You do not say anything, Henry. I think it is because you have a good reason. When have you fenced with him? Henry, you are avoiding my eye. Look up. Tell me the truth: have you fenced with him a single time in the last ten days?"

So far as I was aware I knew nothing about foils, and had never handled them; so I was able to answer, "I will be frank with you, Alice—I haven't."

"I suspected it. Now, Henry, what can you say?"

I was getting some of my wits back, now, and was not altogether unprepared, this time.

"Well, Alice, there hasn't been much fencing weather, and when there was any, I—well, I was lazy, and that is the shameful truth."

"There's a chance now, anyway, and you mustn't waste it. Take off your coat and things."

She rang for George, then she got up and raised the sofa seat and began to fish out boxing gloves, and foils and masks from the locker under it, softly scolding me all the while. George put his head in, noted the preparations, then entered and put himself in boxing trim. It was his turn to take the witness stand, now.

"George, didn't I tell you to keep up Mr. Henry's exercises just the same as if I were about?"

"Yes, madam, you did."

"Why haven't you done it?"

George chuckled, and showed his white teeth and said, "Bless yo' soul, honey, I dasn't."

"Why?"

"Because the first time I went to him—it was that Tuesday, you know, when it was ca'm—he wouldn't hear to it, and said he didn't want no exercise and warn't going to take any, and tole me to go 'long. Well, I didn't stop there, of course, but went to him agin, every now and then, trying to persuade him, till at last he let into me" (he stopped and comforted himself with an unhurried laugh over the recollection of it) "and give me a most solid good cussing, and tole me if I come again he'd take and thow me overboard—there, ain't that so, Mr. Henry?"

My wife was looking at me pretty severely.

"Henry, what have you to say to that?"

It was my belief that it hadn't happened, but I was steadily losing confidence in my memory; and moreover my new policy of recollecting whatever anybody required me to recollect seemed the safest course to pursue in my strange and trying circumstances; so I said, "Nothing, Alice—I did refuse."

"Oh, I'm not talking about that; of course you refused—George had already said so."

"Oh, I see."

"Well, why do you stop?"

"Why do I stop?"

"Yes. Why don't you answer my question?"

"Why, Alice, I've answered it. You asked me—you asked me—what *is* it I haven't answered?"

"Henry, you know very well. You broke a promise; and you are trying to talk around it and get me away from it; but I am not going to let you. You know quite well you promised me you wouldn't swear any more in calm weather. And it is such a little thing to do. It is hardly ever calm, and—"

"Alice, dear, I beg ever so many pardons! I had clear forgotten it; but I won't offend again, I give you my word. Be good to me, and forgive."

She was always ready to forgive, and glad to do it, whatever my crime might be; so things were pleasant again, now, and smooth and happy. George was gloved and skipping about in an imaginary fight, by this time, and Alice told me to get to work with him. She took pencil and paper and got ready to keep game. I stepped forward to position—then a curious thing happened: I seemed to remember a thousand boxing bouts with George, the whole boxing art came flooding in upon me, and I knew just what to do! I was a prey to no indecisions, I had no trouble. We fought six rounds, I held my own all through, and I finally knocked George out. I was not astonished; it seemed a familiar experience. Alice showed no surprise, George showed none; apparently it was an old story to them.

The same thing happened with the fencing. I suddenly knew that I was an experienced old fencer; I expected to get the victory, and when I got it, it seemed but a repetition of something which had happened numberless times before.

We decided to go down to the main saloon and take a regular meal in the regular way—the evening meal. Alice went away to dress. Just as I had finished dressing, the children came romping in, warmly and prettily clad, and nestled up to me, one on each side, on the sofa, and began to chatter. Not about a former home; no, not a word of that, but only about this ship-home and its concerns and its people. After a little I threw out some questions—feelers. They did not understand. Finally I asked them if they had known no home but this one. Jessie said, with some little enthusiasm, "Oh, yes, dream-homes. They are pretty—some of them." Then, with a shrug of her shoulders, "But they are so queer!"

"How, Jessie?"

"Well, you know, they have such curious things in them; and they fade, and don't stay. Bessie doesn't like them at all."

"Why don't you, Bessie?"

"Because they scare me so."

"What is it that scares you?"

"Oh, everything, Papa. Sometimes it is so light. That hurts my eyes. And it's too many lamps—little sparkles all over, up high, and large ones that are dreadful. They could fall on me, you know."

"But I am not much afraid," said Jessie, "because Mama says they are not real, and if they did fall they wouldn't hurt."

"What else do you see there besides the lights, Bessie?"

"Ugly things that go on four legs like our cat, but bigger."

"Horses? Describe them, dear."

"I can't, Papa. They are not alike; they are different kinds; and when I wake up I can't just remember the shape of them, they are so dim."

"And I wouldn't wish to remember them," said Jessie, "they make me feel creepy. Don't let's talk about them, Papa, let's talk about something else."

"That's what I say, too," said Bessie.

So then we talked about our ship. That interested them. They cared for no other home, real or unreal, and wanted no better one. They were innocent witnesses and free from prejudice.

When we went below we found the roomy saloon well lighted and brightly and prettily furnished, and a very comfortable and inviting place altogether. Everything seemed substantial and genuine, there was nothing to suggest that it might be a work of the imagination.

At table the captain (Davis) sat at the head, my wife at his right with the children, I at his left, a stranger at my left. The rest of the company consisted of Rush Phillips, purser, aged

27; his sweetheart the captain's daughter Lucy, aged 22; her sister Connie (short for Connecticut), aged 10; Arnold Blake, surgeon, 25; Harvey Pratt, naturalist, 36; at the foot sat Sturgis the chief mate, aged 35, and completed the snug assemblage. Stewards waited upon the general company, and George and our nurse Germania had charge of our family. Germania was not the nurse's name, but that was our name for her because it was shorter than her own. She was twenty-eight years old, and had always been with us; and so had George. George was thirty, and had once been a slave, according to my record, but I was losing my grip upon that, now, and was indeed getting shadowy and uncertain about all my traditions.

The talk and the feeding went along in a natural way, I could find nothing unusual about it anywhere. The captain was pale, and had a jaded and harassed look, and was subject to little fits of absence of mind; and these things could be said of the mate, also, but this was all natural enough considering the grisly time they had been having, and certainly there was nothing about it to suggest that they were dream-creatures or that their troubles were unreal.

The stranger at my side was about forty-five years old, and he had the half-subdued, half-resigned look of a man who had been under a burden of trouble a long time. He was tall and thin; he had a bushy black head, and black eyes which burned when he was interested, but were dull and expressionless when his thoughts were far away—and that happened every time he dropped out of the conversation. He forgot to eat, then, his hands became idle, his dull eye fixed itself upon his plate or upon vacancy, and now and then he would draw a heavy sigh out of the depths of his breast.

These three were exceptions; the others were chatty and cheerful, and they were like a pleasant little family party together. Phillips and Lucy were full of life, and quite happy, as became engaged people; and their furtive love-passages had everybody's sympathy and approval. Lucy was a pretty creature, and simple in her ways and kindly, and Phillips was a blithe-some and attractive young fellow. I seemed to be familiarly acquainted with everybody, I didn't quite know why. That is, with everybody except the stranger at my side; and as he seemed to know me well, I had to let on to know him, lest I cause remark by exposing the fact that I didn't know him. I was already tired of being caught up for ignorance at every turn.

The captain and the mate managed to seem comfortable

enough until Phillips raised the subject of the day's run, the position of the ship, distance out, and so on; then they became irritable, and sharp of speech, and were unkinder to the young fellow than the case seemed to call for. His sweetheart was distressed to see him so treated before all the company, and she spoke up bravely in his defense and reproached her father for making an offense out of so harmless a thing. This only brought her into trouble, and procured for her so rude a retort that she was consumed with shame, and left the table crying.

The pleasure was all gone, now; everybody felt personally affronted and wantonly abused. Conversation ceased and an uncomfortable silence fell upon the company; through it one could hear the wailing of the wind and the dull tramp of the sailors and the muffled words of command overhead, and this made the silence all the more dismal. The dinner was a failure. While it was still unfinished the company began to break up and slip out, one after another; and presently none was left but me.

I sat long, sipping black coffee and smoking. And thinking; groping about in my dimming land-past an incident of my American life would rise upon me, vague at first, then grow more distinct and articulate, then sharp and clear; then in a moment it was gone, and in its place was a dull and distant image of some long-past episode whose theater was this ship—and then it would develop, and clarify, and become strong and real. It was fascinating, enchanting, this spying among the elusive mysteries of my bewitched memory, and I went up to my parlor and continued it, with the help of punch and pipe, hour after hour, as long as I could keep awake. With this curious result: that the main incidents of both my lives were now recovered, but only those of one of them persistently gathered strength and vividness—our life in the ship! Those of our land-life were good enough, plain enough, but in minuteness of detail they fell perceptibly short of those others; and in matters of feeling—joy, grief, physical pain, physical pleasure—immeasurably short!

Some mellow notes floated to my ear, muffled by the moaning wind—six bells in the morning watch. So late! I went to bed. When I woke in the middle of the so-called day the first thing I thought of was my night's experience. Already my land-life had faded a little—but not the other.

BOOK II

CHAPTER I

I have long ago lost Book I, but it is no matter. It served its purpose—writing it was an entertainment to me. We found out that our little boy set it adrift on the wind, sheet by sheet, to see if it would fly. It did. And so two of us got entertainment out of it. I have often been minded to begin Book II, but natural indolence and the pleasant life of the ship interfered.

There have been little happenings, from time to time. The principal one, for us of the family, was the birth of our Harry, which stands recorded in the log under the date of June 8, and happened about three months after we shipped the present crew, poor devils! They still think we are bound for the South Pole, and that we are a long time on the way. It is pathetic, after a fashion. They regard their former life in the World as their real life and this present one as—well, they hardly know what; but sometimes they get pretty tired of it, even at this late day. We hear of it now and then through the officers—mainly Turner, who is a puzzled man.

During the first four years we had several mutinies, but things have been reasonably quiet during the past two. One of them had really a serious look. It occurred when Harry was a month old, and at an anxious time, for both he and his mother were weak and ill. The master spirit of it was Stephen Bradshaw the carpenter, of course—a hard lot I know, and a born mutineer I think.

In those days I was greatly troubled, for a time, because my wife's memories still refused to correspond with mine. It had been an ideal life, and naturally it was a distress not to be able to live it over again with her in our talks. At first she did not feel about it as I did, and said she could not understand my interest in those dreams, but when she found how much I took the matter to heart, and that to me the dreams had come to have a seeming of reality and were freighted with tender and affectionate impressions besides, she began to change her mind and wish she could go back in spirit with me to the mysterious land. And so she tried to get back that forgotten life. By my help, and by patient probing and searching of her memory she succeeded. Gradually it all came back, and her reward was sufficient. We now had the recollections of two lives to draw upon, and the result was a double measure of happiness for us. We even got the children's former lives back for them—with a good deal of difficulty—next the servants'. It made a new world for us all, and an entertaining one to explore. In the beginning George the colored man was an unwilling subject, because by heredity he was superstitious, and believed that no good could come of meddling with dreams; but when he presently found that no harm came of it his disfavor dissolved away.

Talking over our double-past became our most pleasant and satisfying amusement, and the search for missing details of it our most profitable labor. One day when the baby was about a month old, we were at this pastime in our parlor. Alice was lying on the sofa, propped with pillows—she was by no means well. It was a still and solemn black day, and cold; but the lamps made the place cheerful, and as for comfort, Turner had taken care of that; for he had found a kerosene stove with an isinglass front among the freight, and had brought it up and lashed it fast and fired it up, and the warmth it gave and the red glow it made took away all chill and cheerlessness from the parlor and made it homelike. The little girls were out somewhere with George and Germania (the maid).

Alice and I were talking about the time, twelve years before, when Captain Hall's boy had his tragic adventure with the spider-squid, and I was reminding her that she had misstated the case when she mentioned it to me, once. She had said the squid ate the boy. Out of memory I could call back all the details, now, and I remembered that the boy was only badly hurt, not eaten.

For a month or two the ship's company had been glimpsing vast animals at intervals of a few days, and at first the general terror was so great that the men openly threatened, on two occasions, to seize the ship unless the captain turned back; but by a resolute bearing he tided over the difficulty; and by pointing out to the men that the animals had shown no disposition to attack the ship and might therefore be considered harmless, he quieted them down and restored order. It was good grit in the captain, for privately he was very much afraid of the animals himself and had but a shady opinion of their innocence. He kept his Gatlings in order, and had gun watches, which he changed with the other watches.

I had just finished correcting Alice's history of the boy's adventure with the squid when the ship, plowing through a perfectly smooth sea, went heeling away down to starboard and stayed there! The floor slanted like a roof, and every loose thing in the room slid to the floor and glided down against the bulkhead. We were greatly alarmed, of course. Next we heard a rush of feet along the deck and an uproar of cries and shoutings, then the rush of feet coming back, with a wilder riot of cries. Alice exclaimed, "Go find the children —quick!"

I sprang out and started to run aft through the gloom, and then I saw the fearful sight which I had seen twelve years before when that boy had had his shocking misadventure. For the moment I turned the corner of the deckhouse and had an unobstructed view astern, there it was—apparently two full moons rising close over the stern of the ship and lighting the decks and rigging with a sickly yellow glow—the eyes of the colossal squid. His vast beak and head were plain to be seen, swelling up like a hill above our stern; he had flung one tentacle forward and gripped it around the peak of the mainmast and was pulling the ship over; he had gripped the mizzenmast with another, and a couple more were writhing about dimly away above our heads searching for something to take hold of. The stench of his breath was suffocating everybody.

I was like the most of the crew, helpless with fright; but the captain and the officers kept their wits and courage. The Gatlings on the starboard side could not be used, but the four on the port side were brought to bear, and inside of a minute they had poured more than two thousand bullets into those moons. That blinded the creature, and he let go; and by squirting a violent Niagara of water out of his mouth which tore the sea into a tempest of foam he shot himself backward three hundred yards and the ship forward as far, drowning the deck with a racing flood which swept many of the men off their feet and crippled some, and washed all loose deck-plunder overboard. For five minutes we could hear him thrashing about, there in the dark, and lashing the sea with his giant tentacles in his pain; and now and then his moons showed, then vanished again; and all the while we were rocking and plunging in the booming seas he made. Then he quieted down. We took a thankful full breath, believing him dead.

Now I thought of the children, and ran all about inquiring for them, but no one had seen them. I thought they must have been washed overboard, and for a moment my heart stopped beating. Then the hope came that they had taken refuge with their mother; so I ran there; and almost swooned when I entered the place, for it was vacant. I ran out shouting the alarm, and after a dozen steps almost ran over her. She was lying against the bulwarks drenched and insensible. The surgeon and young Phillips helped me carry her in; then the surgeon and I began to work over her and Phillips rushed away to start the hunt for the children. It was all of half an hour before she showed any sign of life; then her eyes opened with a dazed and wandering look in them, then they recognized me and into them shot a ghastly terror.

"The children! the children!" she gasped; and I, with the heart all gone out of me, answered with such air of truth as I could assume, "They are safe."

I could never deceive her. I was transparent to her.

"It is not true! The truth speaks out all over you—they are lost, oh, they are lost, they are lost!"

We were strong, but we could not hold her. She tore loose from us and was gone in a moment, flying along the dark decks and shrieking the children's names with a despairing pathos that broke one's heart to hear it. We fled after her, and urged that the flitting lanterns meant that all were searching, and begged her for the children's sake and mine if not for her own to go to bed and save her life. But it went for nothing, she would not listen. For she was a mother, and her children were lost. That says it all. She would hunt for them as long as she had strength to move. And that is what she did, hour after hour, wailing and mourning, and touching the hardest hearts with her grief, until she was exhausted and fell in a swoon. Then the stewardess and I put her to bed, and as soon as she came to and was going to creep out of her bed to take up her search again the doctor encouraged her in it and gave her a draught to restore her strength; and it put her into a deep sleep, which was what he expected.

We left the stewardess on watch and went away to join the searchers. Not a lantern was twinkling anywhere, and every figure that emerged from the gloom moved upon tiptoe. I collared one of them and said angrily, "What does this mean? Is the search stopped?"

Turner's voice answered—very low, "—'sh! Captain's orders. The beast ain't dead—it's hunting for us."

It made me sick with fear.

"Do you mean it, Turner? How do you know?

"Listen."

There was a muffled swashing sound out there somewhere,

and then the two moons appeared for a moment, then turned slowly away and were invisible again.

"He's been within a hundred yards of us, feeling around for us with his arms. He could reach us, but he couldn't locate us because he's blind. Once he mighty near had us; one of his arms that was squirming around up there in the dark just missed the foremast, and he hauled in the slack of it without suspecting anything. It made my lungs come up into my throat. He has edged away, you see, but he ain't done laying for us." Pause. Then in a whisper, "He's wallowing around closer to us again, by gracious. Look—look at that. See it? Away up in the air—writhing around like a crooked mainmast. Dim, but—there, now don't you see it?"

We stood dead still, hardly breathing. Here and there at little distances the men were gathering silently together and watching and pointing. The deep hush lay like a weight upon one's spirit. Even the faintest quiver of air that went idling by gave out a ghost of sound. A couple of mellow notes floated lingering and fading down from forward: *Booooom—booooom.* (Two bells in the middle watch.)

A hoarse low voice—the captain's: "Silence that damned bell!"

Instantly there was a thrashing commotion out there, with a thundering rush of discharged water, and the monster came charging for us. I caught my breath, and had to seize Turner or I should have fallen, so suddenly my strength collapsed. Then vaguely we saw the creature, waving its arms aloft, tear past the ship stern first, pushing a vast swell ahead and trailing a tumultuous wake behind, and the next moment it was far away and we were plunging and tossing in the sea it made.

"Thank God, *he's* out of practice!" said Turner, with emotion.

The majestic blind devil stopped out there with its moons toward us, and we were miserable again. We had so hoped it would go home.

I resumed my search. Below I found Phillips and Lucy Davis and a number of others searching, but with no hope. They said they had been everywhere, and were merely going over the ground again and again because they could not bear to have it reported to the mother that the search had ceased. She must be told that they were her friends and that she could depend upon them.

Four hours later I gave it up, wearied to exhaustion, and went and sat down by Alice's bed, to be at hand and support her when she should wake and have to hear my desolate story. After a while she stirred, then opened her eyes and smiled brightly and said, "Oh, what bliss it is! I dreamed that the children—" She flung her arms about me in a transport of grief. "I remember—oh, my God, it is true!"

And so, with sobs and lamentations and frantic self-reproaches she poured out her bitter sorrow, and I clasped her close to me, and could not find one comforting word to say.

"Oh, Henry, Henry, your silence means—oh, we cannot live, we cannot bear it!"

There was a flurry of feet along the deck, the door was burst in, and Turner's voice shouted, "They're found, by God they're found!"

A joy like that brings the shock of a thunderbolt, and for a little while we thought Alice was gone; but then she rallied, and by that time the children were come, and were clasped to her breast, and she was steeped in a happiness for which there were no words. And she said she never dreamed that profanity could sound so dear and sweet, and she asked the mate to say it again; and he did, but left out the profanity and spoiled it.

The children and George and Germania had seen the squid come and lift its moons above our stern and reach its vast tentacle aloft; and they had not waited, but had fled below, and had not stopped till they were deep down in the hold and hidden in a tunnel among the freight. When found, they had had several hours' sleep and were much refreshed.

Between seeing the squid, and getting washed off her feet, and losing the children, the day was a costly one for Alice. It marks the date of her first gray hairs. They were few, but they were to have company.

We lay in a dead calm, and helpless. We could not get away from the squid's neighborhood. But I was obliged to have some sleep, and I took it. I took all I could get, which was six hours. Then young Phillips came and turned me out and said there were signs that the spirit of mutiny was aboard again and that the captain was going to call the men aft and talk to them. Phillips thought I would not want to miss it.

He was right. We had private theatricals, we had concerts, and the other usual time-passers customary on long voyages; but a speech from the captain was the best entertainment the ship's talent could furnish. There was character back of his oratory. He was all sailor. He was sixty years old, and had known no life but sea life. He had no gray hairs, his beard was full and black and shiny; he wore no mustache, therefore his lips were exposed to view; they fitted together like box and lid, and expressed the pluck and resolution that were in him. He had bright black eyes in his old bronze face and they eloquently interpreted all his moods, and his moods were many: for at times he was the youngest man in the ship, and the most cheerful and vivacious and skittish; at times he was the best-natured man in the ship, and he was always the most lovable; sometimes he was sarcastic, sometimes he was serious even to solemnity, sometimes he was stern, sometimes he was as sentimental as a schoolgirl; sometimes he was silent, quiet, withdrawn within himself, sometimes he was talkative and argumentative; he was remarkably and sincerely and persistently pious, and marvelously and scientifically profane; he was much the strongest man in the ship, and he was also the largest, excepting that plotting, malicious and fearless devil, Stephen Bradshaw the carpenter; he could smile as sweetly as a girl, and it was a pleasure to see him do it. He was entirely self-educated, and had made a vast and picturesque job of it. He was an affectionate creature, and in his family relations he was beautiful; in the eyes of his daughters he was omniscient, omnipotent, a mixed sun god and storm god, and they feared him and adored him accordingly. He was fond of oratory, and thought he had the gift of it; and so he practiced it now and then, upon occasion, and did it with easy confidence. He was a charming man and a manly man, with a right heart and a fine and daring spirit.

Phillips and I slipped out and moved aft. Things had an unusual and startling aspect. There were flushes of light here and there and yonder; the captain stood in one of them, the officers stood a little way back of him.

"How do matters stand, Phillips?"

"You notice that the battle lanterns are lit, all the way forward?"

"Yes. The gun watches are at their posts; I see that. The captain means business, I reckon."

"The gun watches are mutineers!"

I steadied my voice as well as I could, but there was still a quaver in it when I said, "Then they've sprung a trap on us, and we are at their mercy, of course."

"It has the look of it. They've caught the old man napping, and we are in a close place this time."

We joined the officers, and just then we heard the measured tramp of the men in the distance. They were coming down from forward. Soon they came into view and moved toward us until they were within three or four paces of the captain.

"Halt!"

They had a leader this time, and it was he that gave the command—Stephen Bradshaw, the carpenter. He had a revolver in his hand. There was a pause, then the captain drew himself up, put on his dignity, and prepared to transact business in a properly impressive and theatrical way. He cleared his voice and said, in a fatherly tone, "Men, this is your spokesman, duly appointed by you?"

Several responded timidly, "Yes, sir."

"You have a grievance, and you desire to have it redressed?"

"Yes, sir."

"He is not here to represent himself, lads, but only you?"

"Yes, sir."

"Very well. Your complaint shall be heard, and treated with justice." [Murmur of approbation from the men.] Then the captain's soft manner hardened a little, and he said to the carpenter, "Go on."

Bradshaw was eager to begin, and he flung out his words with aggressive confidence.

"Captain Davis, in the first place this crew wants to know where they are. Next, they want this ship put about and pointed for home—straight off, and no fooling. They are tired of this blind voyage, and they ain't going to have any more of it—and that's the word with the bark on it." He paused a moment, for his temper was rising and obstructing his breath; then he continued in a raised and insolent voice and with a showy flourish of his revolver. "Before, they've had no leader, and you talked them down and cowed them; but that ain't going to happen this time. And they hadn't any plans, and warn't fixed for business; but it's different, now." He grew exultant. "Do you see this?" His revolver. "And do you see that?" He pointed to the Gatlings. "We've got the guns; we are boss of the ship. Put her about! That's the order, and it's going to be obeyed."

There was an admiring murmur from the men. After a pause the captain said, with dignity, "Apparently you are through. Stand aside."

"Stand aside, is it? Not till I have heard what answer you—"

The captain's face darkened and an evil light began to flicker in his eyes, and his hands to twitch. The carpenter

glanced at him, then stepped a pace aside, shaking his head
and grumbling. "Say your say, then, and cut it short, for I've
got something more to say when you're done, if it ain't
satisfactory."

The captain's manner at once grew sweet, and even tender,
and he turned toward the men with his most genial and
winning smile on his face, and proceeded to take them into
his confidence.

"You want to know where you are, boys. It is reasonable; it
is natural. If we don't know where we are—if we are lost—
who is worst off, you or me? You have no children in this
ship—I have. If we are in danger have I put us there inten-
tionally? Would I have done it purposely—with my children
aboard? Come, what do you think?"

There was a stir among the men, and an approving nodding
of heads which conceded that the point was well taken.

"Don't I know my trade, or am I only an apprentice to it?
Have I sailed the seas for sixty years and commanded ships
for thirty to be taught what to do in a difficulty by—by a
damned carpenter?"

He was talking in such a pleading way, such an earnest, and
moving and appealing way that the men were not prepared
for the close of his remark, and it caught them out and made
some of them laugh. He had scored one—and he knew it. The
carpenter's back was turned—he was playing indifference. He
whirled around and covered the captain with his revolver.
Everybody shrank together and caught his breath, except the
captain, who said gently, "Don't be afraid—pull the trigger; it
isn't loaded."

The carpenter pulled—twice, thrice, and threw the pistol
away. Then he shouted, "Fall back, men—out of the way!"

They surged apart, and he fell back himself. The captain
and the officers stood alone in the circle of light. "Gun 4, fire!"
The officers threw themselves on their faces on the deck, but
the captain remained in his place. The gunner spun the wind-
lass around—there was no result. "Gun 3, fire!" The same
thing happened again. The captain said, "Come back to your
places, men." They obeyed, looking puzzled, surprised, and a
good deal demoralized. The officers got up, looking astonished
and rather ashamed. "Carpenter, come back to your place." He
did it, but reluctantly, and swearing to himself. It was easy to
see that the captain was contented with his dramatic effects.
He resumed his speech, in his pleasantest manner:

"You have mutinied two or three times, boys. It is all right

—up to now. I would have done it myself in my common-seaman days, I reckon, if my ship was bewitched and I didn't know where I was. Now then, can you be trusted with the facts? Are we rational men, manly men, men who can stand up and face hard luck and a big difficulty that has been brought about by nobody's fault, and say live or die, survive or perish, we are in for it, for good or bad, and we'll stand by the ship if she goes to hell!" [The men let go a hearty cheer.] "Are we men—grown men—salt-sea men—men nursed upon dangers and cradled in storms—men made in the image of God and ready to do when He commands and die when He calls—or are we just sneaks and curs and carpenters!" [This brought both cheers and laughter, and the captain was happy.] "There—that's the kind. And so I'll tell you how the thing stands. *I* don't know where this ship is, but she's in the hands of God, and that's enough for me, it's enough for you, and it's enough for anybody but a carpenter. If it is God's will that we pull through, we pull through—otherwise not. We haven't had an observation for four months, but we are going ahead, and do our best to fetch up somewhere."

Eight pages of notes which accompany the manuscript show how Mark Twain intended to continue and end the story. I cannot always be sure which of alternative devices he intended to use, but the following summary rests on a thorough study of the notes in relation to the manuscript.

The mutiny is settled by the captain's acceding to the crew's demand that they turn back. Secretly, however, they falsify the compass and steer by the telltale in Henry's cabin. A month or so later Bradshaw enters the cabin and discovers the fraud. When he brings the men to see it, however, the invisible Superintendent of Dreams holds the needle in the bearing that it should have (north), and the crew lose confidence in Bradshaw.

Jack, the baby who is born just before the mutiny, is weaned at fourteen months. (He is called Harry in the story but Jack in the notes. Reasons for this and other discrepancies are given in my note at the end of this book.) Soon afterward the ship is becalmed. Another ship, the Two Darlings, drifts near. The crews and passengers visit one another. The Two Darlings has a large treasure aboard and Bradshaw, still a conspirator and a mutineer, plans to seize it. A sudden blinding snowstorm strikes, and when it clears the Two Darlings has disappeared. Little Jack and Lucy, the captain's daughter, are on it. Bradshaw, who has thus lost his treasure, demands that they pursue it. The captain and Phillips, Lucy's fiancé, are glad to agree.

The pursuit lasts ten years. Sometimes they sight phantom ships

but can never overtake them nor make them see signals. On board
people are aging, their hair turning gray, and Alice and Henry are
broken by sorrow. Toward the end of the tenth year they come to a
region of "disastrous bright light." (This is the Great White Glare
which Alice has mentioned—and in the scheme of the story it is the
light shining from the microscope's reflector through the slide at
which Henry is looking.) The heat causes intense suffering. (The
reader will remember that Alice's father had been killed by the Glare,
when the ship touched it earlier, and her mother driven to suicide.)
And now the water changes color. (Outside the dream, Alice has put
some Scotch whisky into the drop of water.) The terrible beasts,
which swarm in the Glare, are maddened by the poison and attack
one another and the ship as well. After a terrible fight they are
driven off with the Gatling guns.

Now the sea dries up. "[We] try to walk somewhither but ground
too rough, weather too bad. . . . No shade but in the ship, where they
pant and suffer and long for death." In the distance they see a ship.
The crew are frantic to get the treasure, Alice to save Jack. Henry,
Phillips, the captain, and Bradshaw set out over the rough ocean
floor, carrying water and provisions. But they are too late. The Two
Darlings had run out of provisions long before and everybody on
board is dead, the corpses mummified by the heat. Jack is in Lucy's
arms.

Here the dream becomes nightmare. Phillips and the captain go
mad from grief and Bradshaw, mad also but from thirst, rushes for
the treasure: ". . . sits playing with it and blaspheming. Won't return; will have it all. Tell[s] the men so. Is armed and will kill any
that approach." They leave him there and start back for the ship,
carrying their dead with them. Meanwhile the crew have got drunk
and had a brawl, during which some were killed. "Half-way back we
find the survivors—dying. They started without water."

But worse has happened. "George [the colored servant] on look-
out to prepare me. Stray shot hit Jessie [Henry's oldest child]—she
is dead. I find Alice watching by body. I beg her not to see Jack.
She will. Her grief. Her hair streaked with gray, her face old with
trouble—she is failing fast. Bessie [the other daughter] too. My hair
white. The others in deep gloom. Captain begins to grow violent
when he finds his younger daughter dying, becomes furious with the
dead one [Lucy?]—says 'That is your work, with your cursed voyage.' Two days later all are dead but George and me, and we are
sitting with our dead.

"It is midnight. Alice and the children come to say goodnight. I
think them dreams. Think I am back home in a dream."

That final note brings the story back out of dream and makes the
intended point: dream has triumphed over reality in Henry's mind.

                                                          B. DV.

Editor's Notes

LETTERS FROM THE EARTH

I omit six lines at the end of the first letter. The manuscript breaks off in the middle of a sentence and the omitted lines were preparing a transition to the second letter.

The first letter was called "The Creation of Man," and Paine notes on the manuscript that "Letters from the Earth" (the remaining letters) though suggested by it were "not a continuation of it." Nevertheless the transition is direct and the continuation unmistakable; so I have canceled the first title.

Mark Twain failed to number some of the succeeding letters and gave others fancifully large numbers to suggest, as in "Papers of the Adam Family," that only certain ones had been preserved. I have numbered them consecutively.

Paine briefly discusses the "Letters" on pages 1531-1532 of his *Biography* and quotes something over a page from them.

PAPERS OF THE ADAM FAMILY

I have only my own authority for arranging these sketches in the order given them here and for giving the group the title it appears under. As my running comment indicates, they were written at widely separated times, and only the fourth, fifth, and sixth items have an expressed relationship. I cannot be sure that I have put these three items in the order Mark intended them to have. The manuscripts were in chaos; parts of them, in fact, had been wrongly identified and treated as entirely independent items. Like most of the things that Mark wrote during his last years, they were unfinished, both individually and as a series. They were also intended to have some (to an editor) maddening and altogether nebulous association with a different manuscript called "Book Second," which is too long and in my opinion too dull for inclusion in this book. "Book Second" is a wild fantasy and miscellaneous burlesques dated a thousand years after Mark's death, and it also is unfinished. Themes reappear in it that were sounded in Mark's treatment of the year 920 A.C., and I gather that if both had been developed to scale we should have had, among other things, a history of civilization exemplifying Reginald Selkirk's laws. When I had finally succeeded in piecing the Year 920 papers together it seemed simpler to combine them with sketches to which they are at least formally related than to add to them the inferior "Book Second," from which I take only the title, "Father of History," that is mentioned in my comments.

LETTER TO THE EARTH

The date implied by the sketch itself is the one I have given it, 1887, but it may have been written in the preceding year. Some time later, Mark Twain incorporated it in a manuscript of *A Connecticut Yankee in King Arthur's Court*, making a number of changes to adapt it to the scheme of that book. The changes lengthened and weakened it, however, and he discarded it. I print the earlier version but use the name given the coal dealer in the later one. I also give the sketch a title, Mark having left it without one.

COOPER'S PROSE STYLE

"Fenimore Cooper's Literary Offenses" was written late in 1893 or early in 1894 and published in the *North American Review* for July, 1895. The manuscript supplies the interesting information that both this essay and the previously published one were lectures in a course "prepared for last term by Mark Twain, M.A., Professor of Belles Lettres in the Veterinary College of Arizona." The second lecture was to be preceded by the same quotations that stand at the head of the first: praise of Cooper quoted from Lounsbury, Brander Matthews, and Wilkie Collins.

Whether the Professor of Belles Lettres wrote a third lecture I do not know, but he began one which he numbered IV on Clark Russell's *The Wreck of the Grosvenor*. He abandoned it after writing about a thousand words.

The second lecture was unfinished also, but I have rounded it out with what is unquestionably the original ending of the first one. The manuscript ends with the sentence on page 143, "And it would have almost doubled the effect if the more tempered Cora had done it some, too." What follows that sentence in my text was originally (with an indeterminable amount of lost matter) the original ending of "Fenimore Cooper's Literary Offenses." I do not know why this material was deleted, but assume that, since the essay was overlong for magazine publication, it was cut to make space. In the second paragraph of the published essay Mark alludes to the 114 offenses against literature out of a possible 115 which Cooper scores in a single passage. When he returned to that statement in his concluding paragraphs he gave the essay a unity and a climax that the published text lacks. If a definitive edition of Mark Twain's work is ever published these paragraphs should be restored to their original context.

SIMPLIFIED SPELLING

The date I assign this sketch, 1906, is the one when it was interpolated in a dictation for Mark Twain's autobiography. It was certainly written before that day but how long before I have no way of knowing. In fact, I am not altogether sure that it has not been previously published. There is a memorandum of a pamphlet on simplified spelling which I cannot identify or trace.

FROM AN ENGLISH NOTEBOOK

The reader will find an account of Mark Twain's visit to England, of the notebooks made during it, and other extracts from them in Paine's *Biography*, pages 458-471. Paine prints part of the passage on the British Museum which I have thought sufficiently interesting to print in full. He appears to have had access either to another notebook than the one which remains in the Papers or to the original entries from it which Mark mailed to Mrs. Clemens from England, for I cannot find some of the items he quotes.

THE FRENCH AND THE COMANCHES

This sketch is one of several chapters on French civilization that were left out of the book, together with chapters on Heidelberg, Munich, and Switzerland and several unrelated sketches that had been interpolated. In all the French chapters Mark Twain conducts his inquiry as a study in comparative anthropology, defending France on the ground that it is fully as advanced as any other semicivilized nation. Although the other chapters are occasionally amusing and have some biographical importance, they seem to me too thin for inclusion in this book.

FROM AN UNFINISHED BURLESQUE OF BOOKS
ON ETIQUETTE

Paine quotes a few passages (which I do not reprint) from this manuscript on pages 705-706 of his *Biography*. He seems not to have appreciated the intention of the burlesque, however. Mark was satirizing not manners but the manuals of deportment plentifully provided for the Plush Age. Paine dates the manuscript 1881 but its appearance suggests that Mark's interest was intermittent and that he returned to it several times. I print less than half of it here.

THE DAMNED HUMAN RACE

It has seemed desirable to include in this book representative specimens of the philosophical sketches which Mark Twain wrote during his last years as a kind of cumulative annotation of *What Is Man?* and *The Mysterious Stranger*. There are many such sketches in the Mark Twain Papers, some completed, more left unfinished. Not many of them treat material that will be new to a student of Mark's work but there are many passages of great force and charm. The first of my selections, for instance, is in his best vein.

Three of these pieces, and probably all of them, belong to the period 1905-1909. The comment on Zola, however, may be several years earlier and, as my footnote says, the last selection may go back to 1897. Mr. Paine quotes from the first and fifth selections in his

Biography, apparently following earlier texts than those preserved in the Papers. I have provided the titles of the last three.

THE GREAT DARK

Mark Twain did not give this story a title. Paine labeled the manuscript "Statement of the Edwardses," a title which seems to me not only inept but misrepresentative. Since it is not Mark's, I have felt free to substitute for it a phrase taken from one of his notes.

A proper editorial comment on "The Great Dark" would require much more space than can be spared here. The various ideas that make up the story troubled Mark almost obsessively for two years, some of them go back many years in his notebooks, all of them were obviously important to him, and he tried to work them out in various ways. These facts and the story itself have important implications.

The reader will have noticed several discrepancies in the story. I have already called attention to the confusion about the name of Henry's child. This was only a slight lapse but my summary of Mark's proposed ending (which is based on the last notes for the story, some of them probably made while Mark was writing it) indicates that he either had forgotten or was ignoring more important circumstances of the dream. For instance, Henry says at the beginning of Book II that the manuscript of Book I had been lost, whereas the whole scheme of the narrative requires it to be preserved, as in fact the story preserves it. Again, Henry is vague and even contradictory about the lapse of time between the two books and, what is more important, the whole orientation of the story changes between the two parts. And finally neither the story nor the notes answer a question which is crucial to Mark's conception; at what time, in relation to the dream, did Henry write his narrative? We are left to infer that he did so between the time when Alice broke the decanter and the "it is midnight" of the last note. But this inference, which is supported by the opening of Book I, renders incomprehensible the note "and I have finished writing this," which is included within the dream.

Such discrepancies must be regarded as vestiges left from earlier stages of three principal ideas and of the stories in which he tried to embody them. The ideas are: the confusion of dream and reality, the brief actual duration of dreams that may seem to last for many years, and the fate of a ship's company lost for years in the storms of a fabulous portion of the Antarctic. All three ideas are fused in "The Great Dark" but I cannot find that all three of them came together in any of the earlier, unfinished, and abandoned stories.

On August 16, 1898 (Letters page 644), Mark writes to Howells that he has at last found the right way to write a story which he had not found at the end of ten thousand words written the year before. It was a story which was to be called "Which Was the Dream?" and whose central idea he had told to Howells in confidence "three or four years ago." The letter implies but does not say clearly that he tried to write it during the summer of 1897 but had to abandon it.

Now, however, he has found the right way to write it and it has begun "to slide from the pen with ease and confidence." But if Howells should see a little story called "My Platonic Sweetheart" (another dream story which, his notebook shows, was finished ten days before this letter) "*that* is not this one."

Unhappily the story he is talking about does not seem to be "The Great Dark," either, in any recognizable form. The title suggests the confusion of dream and reality and that idea is clearly adumbrated by the notes I have already quoted, but it does not seem to have entered into "The Great Dark" until six days before the letter to Howells nor to have been actually applied to a revision of the already existing story until five weeks after the letter. Whereas, though no manuscript called "Which Was the Dream?" is among the Mark Twain Papers, there is a note (to be dated only by conjecture) which indicates that there was once such a story or at least a well worked-out plan for it—and the story described in that note is radically different from "The Great Dark" and has only a slight relationship to it.

Over a year before the letter to Howells Mark wrote in a notebook, "May 23, 1897. Wrote first chapter of above story today." In his *Biography* (pages 1041-1042) Mr. Paine says that the "above story" was about a man who dozes for a moment and is led, by the smell of his burning cigarette, to dream of the destruction of his family and "a long period of years following. Awakening a few seconds later, and confronted by his wife and children, he refuses to believe in their reality, maintaining that this condition, and not the other, is the dream." He then says that Mark attempted to work out the same idea in the story published here as "The Great Dark." I am not sure, however, that Mr. Paine is right. Unless Mark Twain told him the story that was to elaborate the note (which is possible) or unless he had access to a manuscript which has since disappeared or been destroyed (which is unlikely) he both overinterprets the note and makes a serious mistake about it. The idea of the brief duration of the dream is certainly present in "The Great Dark" and a story embodying it is certainly indicated by the note. But, although the note does not actually mention the destruction of a home by fire which Mr. Paine has got from somewhere else, it certainly has nothing to do with a sea voyage. And a more important consideration is that it is not the note next "above" the entry of May 23. Between note and entry there is another note and this one lists characters for a story about a voyage. If Mr. Paine is right about the story based on the first of the two notes, then he is certainly wrong in identifying it as the one which Mark began on May 23, 1897. And in my judgment it was not. I interpret the first of the two notes, whether or not it was ever developed into a story, as another recurrence of the idea assigned to "Which Was the Dream?" I interpret the second as relating to a quite separate story, one which Mark did indeed begin when he says he did, and one which, whether it can be identified or not, was closely related to a series of stories about voyages in more or less enchanted waters, a series which did not incorporate the other ideas that were troubling Mark's mind until he wrote "The Great Dark" in September or October, 1898.

Here it is possible to come out of the conjectural for a while. In August, 1897, Mark made a number of notes for a story about a ship that got caught in a kind of Antarctic Sargasso, an area of everlasting gales and snowstorms, in whose very center was a smaller area of everlasting calm through which other ships drifted forever. (If his letter to Howells of a year later did not speak so positively of "Which Was the Dream?" I should be fairly confident that the ten thousand words he had written during that summer were a development of these notes.) The background is extensively worked up, the earlier history of the characters is noted in detail, and preparations are made for an elaborate plot which was also to be an apologue with social and philosophical implications. These notes have an unmistakable bearing on "The Great Dark" and there is a strong temptation to associate them with the letter to Howells. Previously to writing them, moreover, he had written at least one story, and very possibly two, just as clearly related to the one he was now planning. At the end of 1896 or very early in 1897 he had written into the manuscript of *Following the Equator* a story that purported to be the narrative of a sailor who had once been caught in the eternal storms and the eternal calm at their center. (The storm area was called the Devil's Race Track and the central calm the Everlasting Sunday.) He called this sketch "The Enchanted Sea-Wilderness" but did not finish it and had to omit it from his book.

I cannot prove that the second story was written when I believe it was, immediately after *Following the Equator*. Proof, if it is possible at all, must await a prolonged study of many other manuscripts and notes that cannot be considered here. But my present belief is that it developed from the second of two notebook entries I have already mentioned, that it was the story whose "first chapter" Mark wrote on May 23, 1897. It is called "An Adventure in Remote Seas," and in it a sealing ship is driven far into the Antarctic by long-continued storms. It has nothing to do with the Devil's Race Track, but half of the ship's company are abandoned on an uncharted island when another storm drives the vessel out to sea. The theme of "The Enchanted Sea-Wilderness," which is also one of the themes of "The Great Dark," is thus repeated in variation—and in a cave on the island the crew find an enormous treasure of gold coins (note the treasure carried by the *Two Darlings*). That is as far as the manuscript goes but the notes for its continuation show that, like the story outlined by the notes of August, 1897, it was to be a fable. It was to embody a sermon in intrinsic value and a tract favoring the free coinage of silver!

We have so far, then, the sailor's story about the Everlasting Sunday and the ships becalmed in it and manned by corpses, the sealing-ship story in which the Antarctic waste holds a vast treasure (if my guess about its date may be accepted), and the notes of August, 1897, which outline an intricately wrought story of a ship's company living out their lives in the Everlasting Sunday. It is important to note that none of these stories is told as a dream, that in fact no dream enters into any of them. That is what makes Mark's letter to Howells so baffling. If he had been writing a story about the confusion of dream and reality, there is no unequivocal evidence that it also concerned a voyage in enchanted seas or had any other direct bearing on "The Great Dark."

Both "The Enchanted Sea-Wilderness" and the final notes for "The Great Dark" develop the idea of being eternally becalmed and encountering the mummified bodies of earlier voyagers who had met the same fate. It had been working in Mark's mind for a long time. As far back as 1882, when he revisited the Mississippi, he made a notebook entry in which the idea appears. Here, however, the scene is a balloon caught in a level of the upper air from which there is no escape. Mr. Willis Wager informs me that a short burlesque worked up from this note was actually written into the manuscript of Life on the Mississippi. I have some reason for believing that it may go back further than that—to the early stages of "Captain Stormfield's Visit to Heaven," in the late 1860's. Without attaching too much importance to the similarity, one may remember that the famous cave at Hannibal contained a copper cylinder in which an eccentric physician had preserved his daughter's body in alcohol. But whatever its private meaning to Mark, the idea had so firmly taken hold of him that, though only the Antarctic cold can rationally explain the mummies, he carries it over to "The Great Dark" and explains that the heat of the Great Glare has preserved them.

On August 10, 1898, Mark writes in his notebook:

> Last night dreamed of a whaling cruise in a drop of water. Not by microscope, but *actually*. This would mean a reduction of the participants to a minuteness which would make them nearly invisible to God and he wouldn't be interested in them any longer.
> Lying thinking about this, concluded to write a dispute between a microscope and a telescope—one can pull a moral out of that.

This entry is crucial in the development we are following. It has one discordant—and exasperating—implication. The second sentence might imply that he had been thinking about a whaling cruise in a drop of water previously to this date, and that the voyage was to be made by microscope. If he had been, no evidence has survived, and if he wrote anything embodying the idea the manuscript is not in the Mark Twain Papers. However that may be, six days later than the note, Mark writes to Howells that he has now found the right way to write the story he had been unable to finish a year ago. It is now sliding from the pen "with ease and confidence." Was this story some version of "The Great Dark"? If it was, what was the version which he had been unable to write in the summer of 1897 and had abandoned at the end of ten thousand words?

Several notations may be made here. In the first place, the second sentence of the note does not absolutely require the inference I have suggested above, and in fact I do not believe that he had been thinking about a voyage in a drop of water before this dream. My present hypothesis is that this dream was the stimulus which, in the course of the next six weeks, fused his three principal ideas in "The Great Dark" but that, when he wrote to Howells, that fusion was not yet complete. I think that the story which now began to slide so easily from his pen was at first a variant of either our X ("Which Was the Dream?," mentioned in the letter to Howells) or our Y, the story presumably written from the notes of August, 1897. I think, that is, that it was not an immediately related variant of "The Great Dark." And I think, furthermore, that Mark's letter to Howells shows either a faulty memory of what he had done the year before or an as yet unclarified understanding of what he was doing now.

(That last hypothesis is not so wild as it may seem at first glance. As I have shown, Mark did not remember the name of Henry's child from the actual draft of his story to the notes for its completion. Tom Sawyer's name is Bob Sawyer in the first sketch of the story [Mark Twain Papers] and though that alteration may have been deliberate, the published text of *The Adventures of Tom Sawyer* shows an insoluble confusion about Becky Thatcher's family relationships and even about her home town, a confusion which is increased in *Adventures of Huckleberry Finn.* What is more striking, when he came to write *Huckleberry Finn* Mark did not remember the name of Tom's sweetheart and did not even pick up a copy of *Tom Sawyer* to verify it in, so that she has always been Bessie Thatcher in Huck's story. There is even some evidence that between the two books he had forgotten who had undertaken to break Huck to gentility, that he assigned that function to Miss Watson, and that, later remembering the Widow Douglas, he had to make his newly invented character her sister [Mark Twain Papers].

Whatever he may have written with such ease and confidence following the dream and the letter to Howells, we again emerge from speculation and conjecture on September 21, 1898. On that day he made another long series of notes which are obviously related to the dream and even more obviously related to "The Great Dark." The dream had dealt with a cruise in a drop of water and so do these notes. It is important that a few of the early ones are concerned with the dimensions necessitated by the reduced scale—and clearly state that this voyage is to occur under a microscope. It is even more important that' they take the material of the notes made thirteen months before, in August, 1897, and convert it to the action of a dream story. This is the first time that the voyage in enchanted waters, with its related tableaus of mummified corpses, has occurred *in a dream.* That is the crucial step in the development of the story: it seemed to solve the difficulty that had probably made him abandon both "The Enchanted Sea-Wilderness" and "An Adventure in Remote Seas"; it provided a way of getting the ship out of the Antarctic waste. What is equally important, it captured by attraction the two other ideas he had been trying to work out, the brief duration of dreams in which many years seem to elapse and the confusion of dream and reality. And, I think, it followed directly from Mark's own dream of August 9. (If I am right, then the scholarly need not play with the theorem that Mark was "influenced" by Fitz-James O'Brien's "The Diamond Lens," though I must conscientiously record that Thomas Bailey Aldrich was a friend of O'Brien's and once told Mark an amusing anecdote about him which was duly deposited in the notebooks.)

There remained one further transformation and Mark made it in another, later set of notes, those which accompany the manuscript of "The Great Dark" and from which the story was written. One of the ships in this dream was to carry a great treasure, such as there had been in "An Adventure in Remote Seas" and in the note which is the sole demonstrable reference to a story called "Which Was the Dream?" The story he had been trying to tell in so many apparently unrelated ways now seemed clear in his mind. Henry Edwards was to dream briefly—for a few seconds or a few minutes. He was to dream of a voyage in a drop of water which would take him to a place of everlasting darkness and storm. He was to be caught there for many years, during which he was to have many horrible experiences, among them a maddened pursuit of a treasure-ship. He was to succumb to the dream and, on waking from it, was to believe not only that many years had passed but also that the reality to which he had awakened was a hallucination and his dream the reality.

The story was begun, I think, soon after the notes of September 21, 1898. I have no way of knowing how long he worked on it, but eventually this version also proved unwritable. The idea had been urgent to the verge of obsession, but this attempt like the others had to be given up. I have mentioned his frequent inability to think the material of fiction into appropriate form, and that inability is evident here. Reasons why it may have been increased at this time will occur to anyone who knows Mark Twain's personal history during the 1890's. And there is one other reason for this particular failure: in spite of his interest in the ideas of the story, in spite of their obvious importance to him, he at no time clearly phrased to himself what he was trying to do with it. As always, his fertile imagination produced many kinds of scenes, many characters, and much action, but he was vague about the ultimate bearing of the story. Why? The answer is to be found not in the story itself but in the plain bearing of its materials. Quite clearly, "The Great Dark" was, psychologically, a stage on the way to *The Mysterious Stranger.*

In the early part of the story Mark tries to sustain the feeling of dream imagery. The confusion of nautical terms is appropriate to the half-aware irrelevance of a dream, and so is the striking combination of a sea chantey and a Negro spiritual which the sailors sing when they are "sheeting home." More striking is the figure of the Superintendent of Dreams. (Kipling's "Brushwood Boy" was published in the *Century* for December, 1895, but I cannot see that it had the slightest influence on this story.) The Superintendent's appearances and disappearances, his antics and moods, his mysterious balefulness are all dreamlike. He first comes into the notes (those of September, 1898) as a footprint that sometimes appears on the deck, always as an omen of some terrible event to come. Later he is conceived as the architect and stage manager of the dream, which is what he is in the story actually written. But other notes assign him a still more prominent role and he is clearly an unconscious anticipation of Satan in *The Mysterious Stranger.*

Mark's ambivalent thinking about the Superintendent is characteristic. Here was a very usable character, but exactly what use to make of him was never certain, was something to be worked out by trial and error. He is abandoned entirely in Book II except for the note that has him, in the continuation which Mark did not write, holding the needle of the telltale in a false bearing when Bradshaw brings the crew into Henry's cabin. And the use actually made of him shows another confusion that is typical of Mark's literary thinking. (I have discussed it at length in *Mark Twain's America.*) His horseplay with the mate's coffee is no doubt true to the emotions of the dream state but it is also wildly out of tune with this story. It introduces burlesque into a somber, even terrible narrative. Henry's boxing and fencing with George similarly threaten, and for some readers must destroy, the illusion that has been so carefully built up. They suggest some of the apparent improvisations of the last quarter of *Huckleberry Finn,* and, like them, were carefully and enthusiastically planned. [Mark Twain Papers.] Mark says in the letter to Howells already quoted, "I feel sure that all of the first half of the story—and I hope three-fourths—will be comedy; but by the former plan the whole of it (except the first 3 chapters) would have been tragedy and unendurable, almost. I think I can carry the reader a long way before he suspects that I am laying a tragedy trap." This attempt to combine burlesque with "unendurable" tragedy was a serious error in aesthetic judgment but was absolutely in character, for the same error had damaged much of his fiction before this. In effect, whenever he failed to think a conception through its own terms his usual instinct was to turn to burlesque.

There was one further uncertainty and, reaching it, I must account for the editing I have done on the manuscript. I have said that Mark did not clearly understand what he was trying to do with the various themes and situations that went into this story. All except one of them are fused in it as it is published here. That one was not successfully combined with the others until *The Mysterious Stranger* but he tried to combine it with them in "The Great Dark."

In "An Adventure in Remote Seas" and in the notes of August, 1897, there is an intermittent but clear intention to provide the story with satirical comments on manners, morals, customs, superstitions, and injustices in society. Mark was afflicted with the same intention when he began to write "The Great Dark" and it was not until he became dissatisfied with the satire that he went back, removed it, and rewrote the story as the pure fantasy it now is.

The vehicle of this social satire was the Mad Passenger (sometimes called the Crazy Passenger in the earliest notes), who is the "stranger at my side" when the company sit down to dinner near the present end of Book I. Following the captain's rebuke to his daughter, which is where the rewritten version begins to diverge from the original one, Henry becomes friendly with the Mad Passenger and forms the habit of dropping into his cabin for conversation. He is a native of one of the floating Empires that circle drifting forever "outside the Great White Glare and just the right distance away from it." It is through him that Henry begins to learn more about Dreamland, one of whose unreal planets, the World, Henry appears to have visited. All "dreamlands were nothing but imitations of real countries created out of the dreamer's own imagination and experience, with some help perhaps from the Superintendent of Dreams." (*The Mysterious Stranger* quivers toward birth in that assertion.) In the opinion of the Mad Passenger, the crew and officers are mad, for they are trying to steer the ship by a chart of Dreamland, very likely one of the World. From the conversation on shipboard he has come to understand that civilization in that part of Dreamland is not much different from what it is in his Empire. But there are interesting differences. In his native language, for instance, there are no words for ideas he has encountered here: modesty, immodesty, decency, indecency, right, wrong, etc. And the World is unique among dreamlands, he says, in having what "they term Religions; also curious systems of government and an interesting but most odd code of morals."

There is an excellent moment when, to entertain Henry's children, the Mad Passenger sets up a microscope. "A curious feeling came over me. It seemed to me that I had seen the same thing done before; even that I had done it myself—in a dream. It was a strange sensation, and troubled me. Then the Mad Passenger put a drop of water on a glass slide, threw a circle of white light under it from the reflector, screwed the lens down tight against it, and soon the children were exclaiming over the hideous animals they saw darting about and fighting in the bit of moisture." This is well conceived and one is sorry that Mark did not keep it when he changed his scheme.

The Mad Passenger had been aboard the ship for twenty-two years and has no hope of revisiting his country. He is here as a result of taking some friends to cruise in the great darkness. In a snow squall he was swept off his yacht and aboard the passing ship. The years of longing have taught him to endure his exile with fortitude. . . . One day, in his absence, Henry picks up a portfolio which contains drawings and photographs of the Mad Passenger, his family, and ladies and gentlemen obviously his friends—"in some cases beautifully clothed but in most cases naked." A moment later, "I heard him coming. I put the book away and prepared myself to look like a person who had not discovered a disgraceful secret and who was not shocked. I arranged a pleasant smile and . . ."

Here the Mad Passenger manuscript ends. Its intent is obvious. Mark had begun "The Great Dark" intending to use a device which he had used so often before, which he was soon to use again in *The Mysterious Stranger* and later in "Letters from the Earth," a traveler making observations on the illogicalities and absurdities of human civilization.

After deciding to abandon this satirical device, he rewrote the story from the dinner on to the present end. He deleted from the manuscript all the preceding preparation for the Mad Passenger story except occasional touches which, on the assumption that their retention was inadvertent, I have dropped out. But he also, either then or at some later time, made other revisions and marked still other passages for modification. Wherever I can be sure of his revisions I have followed them in this text. In passages where I am not sure—passages which are either rewritten in a way that does not seem to make sense or are marked for revision but not revised throughout —I have had to adopt the reading that seems most appropriate to the final form of the story. Practically all of these passages—there are a good many of them—occur in Book I.

Readers who know the details of Mark's life will have discovered that some of them are reproduced in "The Great Dark." For instance, Mark twice crossed the Atlantic in the *Batavia*, once alone and once with his family, and when Henry reminds Alice that she was attended during an illness by the author of *Rab and His Friends* all the details he mentions are taken from Mark's experience. In the notes there are occasional hints of a deliberate intention to make the story represent his own life. Most of them are not developed in the story, and those which are developed are modified so much that one may safely say he abandoned the plan. Nevertheless both the difficulty he had writing "The Great Dark" and the obstinacy with which he kept coming back to it suggest that it meant more to him than a mere story, that its basic fantasies were extremely important to him. I have pointed out that he was making toward *The Mysterious Stranger*, a more successful treatment of the same themes, but it is also true that he was here expressing the dread and sorrow of the preceding six years of his life. "The Great Dark" is therefore important in his artistic biography.

Bibliographical Note

"GLANCES AT HISTORY," second fragment, was published by Bernard DeVoto in *The Saturday Review of Literature* (XIX, 4, December 10, 1938).

"LETTER TO THE EARTH" was published by DeVoto in *Harper's Magazine* (CXCII, 106-109, February, 1946) and in *Report from Paradise*, ed. Dixon Wecter, Harper & Brothers, New York, 1952, pp. 87-94, under the title "Letter from the Recording Angel."

"A CAT-TALE" was published in *Concerning Cats*, ed. Frederick Anderson, The Book Club of California, San Francisco, 1959, pp. 1-19.

"COOPER'S PROSE STYLE" was edited by DeVoto for publication in *New England Quarterly* (XIX, 291-301, September, 1946) under the title "Fenimore Cooper's Further Literary Offenses."

"THE GORKY INCIDENT" was edited by DeVoto for publication in *Slavonic and East European Review* (XXII, part 2, 37-38, August, 1944).

"THE GREAT DARK" was published in part (i.e., about 2,800 words) by DeVoto in his *Mark Twain at Work*, Harvard University Press, Cambridge, 1942, pp. 133-140.

74 1